Y0-ARR-680

PARTS AND WHOLES

PARTS AND WHOLES

The Hayden Colloquium on Scientific Method and Concept

EDITED BY

DANIEL LERNER

CONTRIBUTORS

Roman Jakobson
Clyde Kluckhohn
Simon Kuznets
Daniel Lerner
Ernest Nagel
Edward Purcell
Simon Ramo
I. A. Richards

NEW YORK : THE FREE PRESS OF GLENCOE
LONDON : MACMILLAN NEW YORK

Printed in the United States of America

For information, address:

The Free Press of Glencoe
A Division of The Macmillan Company,
The Crowell-Collier Publishing Company
60 Fifth Avenue, New York 11

Collier-Macmillan Canada, Ltd.,
Galt, Ontario

Library of Congress Catalog Card Number: 63–7658

To the memory of
CLYDE KLUCKHOHN

PREFACE

THE HAYDEN COLLOQUIUM of the Massachusetts Institute of Technology is a distinguished lecture series concerned with common problems of concept and method in the diverse fields of modern knowledge. Each year the Colloquium selects a classic theme that has preoccupied thinkers over many generations, sometimes over centuries. The lecturers are asked to clarify the meaning of this classic theme for contemporary work in their own field of knowledge. How are the problems historically associated with this theme encountered by living people concerned with theory, research, and judgment in fields ranging from aesthetics to zoology? How have new versions of the old problems been set and met? To what extent is the traditional formulation of these problems no longer relevant to contemporary needs? In instances in which the contemporary formulation is more amenable to current thinking, but is so stated as to leave the older problem unsolved, what importance has the unsolved residue?

To questions such as these our lecturers respond in terms of work in progress, and their responses are critically discussed by the members of the Colloquium. This practice has produced over the years a continuing conversation among the various fields of knowledge and common problems of considerable breadth and depth have emerged. It has appeared worth while to preserve the final form of these lectures in book form. Our first and second Colloquiums were published by The Free Press as *Evidence and Inference* and *Quantity and Quality*, respectively.

The making of such a book represents the cooperative work of many hands. The lecture series has been sponsored by the M.I.T. School of Humanities and Social Studies, from funds granted by the Carnegie Corporation of New York. Dean John E. Burchard made the Colloquium possible and has been a firm supporter of its continuance.

The papers in this volume are based on lectures delivered to the

Hayden Colloquium. In three cases, the discussion that followed the lecture was sufficiently interesting (and the tape-recording sufficiently clear) to warrant inclusion. These convey some sense of the intellectual style of the meetings, and in several places sharpen the philosophical or scientific issues arising from the lectures. The paper by Ernest Nagel is reprinted here by the kind permission of the editors of *Philosophical Studies*.

On behalf of his colleagues in the Hayden Colloquium, in which he participated vigorously from its inception, I wish to express our profound sense of loss in the untimely passing of Clyde Kluckhohn. On the occasion of his lecture to the Hayden Colloquium, here published, he was described as "the intellectual conscience of anthropology." This suggests the quality that made him, for workers in many fields, a priceless teacher and a cherished colleague.

The Hayden Colloquium was originally planned as a three-year exploration among classic problems of scientific concept and method set in a contemporary research framework. *Parts and Wholes* completes the triad initiated by *Evidence and Inference* and continued by *Quantity and Quality*. The exploration has been found rewarding by its participants; accordingly, a fourth Colloquium on "Cause and Effect" was held during 1960–1961 and will be published in due course.

DANIEL LERNER

CONTENTS

PARTS AND WHOLES

INTRODUCTION

On Parts and Wholes

DANIEL LERNER

ST. PAUL, much troubled by the partial character of human knowledge, imagined paradise as a state in which one would know wholly: "For now we see through a glass, darkly; but then face to face: now I know in part; but then I shall know even as also I am known" (I Corinthians xiii.11). Partial knowledge, St. Paul warned in the same Epistle to the Corinthians, misleads us into inaccurate conclusions and incorrect actions: "For we know in part, and we prophesy in part."

This troubled aspect of empirical knowledge—that it deals with parts and not wholes—has persisted into our own days. Even our physicists—and none within the scientific community have been more alert to the fundamental philosophical questions—have produced no completely satisfying remedy for the trouble. Are quantum states, for example, genuinely "qualitative" mutants in natural continua, or are they only "quantitative" discontinuities in statistical continua that we do not know how to explain? A working solution proposed by Victor Weisskopf, who faced this question in last year's Hayden Colloquium on "Quantity and Quality," is that a discontinuity that cannot be explained quantitatively had better be dealt with as a qualitative change—as, in some significant relationship to its parts, a different "whole."

Edward Purcell opens this year's Hayden Colloquium by taking the quantum theory of physical behavior into a discussion that revives and illuminates the ancient problem of "Parts and Wholes" in terms that are fundamental for modern science. The consistent modesty of Purcell's formulation is a lesson in epistemology (as well as personal style) because it reopens for questioning the logic of empirical inquiry—its scope and limits. The specific question he puts to us, in presenting the Ising problem as a "model for models," is: Under what conditions do parts want to behave like their neighboring parts—and what difference does this make in the whole to which all these parts belong?

Purcell's answer conveys a profound lesson to all of us precisely because the example he has selected is not, as he insists, a profound one. As the discussion of his paper brought out, the solution lies in the "superficial" (by definition) field of topology. But topology, if it deals with surfaces, ends by eliciting their complexity and revealing the subtlety of intellectual means needed to cope with them. The solution, as Purcell presents it, has some elegance. Merely to know that the parts are "identical" (in terms of the particular identity assigned to them), and that a rudimentary principle of order activates them (like wanting to point the same way as their neighbors at the Curie point in temperature), is enough to provide a means of solving a deep problem of physical behavior—in this case, magnetism. But what a "merely" this confronts us with!

Most of the sciences have lacked the persistence, and perhaps also the clarity, of physics in positing contextual units (for example, temperature and pressure) that make possible deep adjudication of variations in particular behavior. Accordingly, when asked to identify a set of "identical parts" and some rudimentary "principle of order" that activates them, many other sciences are likely to shrug and go fishing. Their problem is still how to define "wholes" in such fashion as to make differences of empirical behavior meaningful. The task varies in difficulty, of course, with the scope and limits of the problems each science seeks to solve. The first four papers in this volume illustrate the diverse order of complexity in the defining structure of several disciplines.

The matter is philosophically simpler in economics, according to Simon Kuznets, since "the wholes are artificial species of 'ideal types' created to facilitate economic study." Any such "whole," defined to suit the convenience of research specialists, can be studied "without continuous reference to the relation of this particular institution or process to a still wider whole of which it is a part and within whose framework it must operate." Economics thus avoids the extreme complexity of anthropological wholes, which seek to construct from constituent parts "in their totality" a cultural configuration of "ultimate and irreducible distinctiveness." Economics, on the contrary, is content with the more operational view that "the choice of the whole depends on the problem that the economic analyst wishes to study."

Empirical procedures, however, do generate some rather difficult problems, as Kuznets explains: "But the selection of the specific parts that will reveal analytically significant differences is a problem in itself—because the choice is guided by existing knowledge and the hypotheses that it generates, and, since current knowledge is incomplete, we may overlook important parts and distinctions." The point is that the distinction of parts in economics, which is designed to improve analysis and understanding of the whole, depends *ab initio* upon the existing state of knowledge of the whole.

This is a more complex situation than that faced by a physicist, who starts by knowing everything necessary about his parts (that is, that they are all electrons of the same atom), and knows, or hypothesizes, the fundamental principle of behavior that explains their interaction as a whole. The economist cannot identify economic particles, or the principle of interaction that governs them, in such simple and comprehensive fashion. Certain situations can be localized that impose a "forced choice" between mutually exclusive behavioral principles in a manner that resembles the choice of pointing the same way or not that Purcell gave his little magnets. For example, in a true "market" situation, the relationship among parts "is one of competition when the parts are on the same side of the supply-demand equation, or one of bargaining when they are on opposite sides." But the results obtained "with the help of broadly assumed principles of action within some empirically constrained conditions of operation" become meaningful with reference to quite a different model than that proposed by Purcell.

The fundamental application of the economic model, Kuznets tells us, is to determine the interaction between individuals and society: "The ever-present intellectual puzzle that confronts economic study is how to explain the social result in terms of individual actions; the purpose of the long chain of connections that runs from the individual to the firm to the industry to the region to the nation, or from the individual to his economic class to the nation, and other varieties of grouping and linking, is the better specification and analysis of the relation between the two termini of the chain." Kuznets thus poses squarely the core problem of "behavioral science" —that the behavior of individual human beings is a "whole" whose parts do not necessarily coincide with the analytic units that are most convenient for economists (or other specialized observers). Even those situations that lie most clearly within the economist's domain present deep problems of method—disaggregation, cumulation and comparability, and change over time. But the fundamental problem arises from the fact that economic activity occurs within a larger matrix of individual behavior and social constraints. Within larger units, such as the nation, noneconomic elements are more important in shaping economic activity than elements amenable to economic analysis. Kuznets states this point forcefully:

> Granted that we can measure the economic results of cooperation within such a unit and some aspects of its structure, our analytical tools are not adequate for explaining their formation and their capacity to provide conditions for economic growth or other desirable patterns of economic behavior. We face here a fundamental question whether economics as a separate discipline can deal with the economic behavior of such larger units—a question that can perhaps be paralleled by one concerning the usefulness of economics in dealing with the household unit, also much affected by major noneconomic considerations. But this means that, in its structure of wholes and of parts, and its assumed conditions and principles of operation, economics deals with only a part of the economic process, with only a part of the social relations that have grown up about the production of material means for satisfying wants; and sometimes not the most important but only the most analyzable parts.

Dr. Simon Ramo takes us from the universe of scientific theory, as discussed by Kuznets and Purcell, into the new field of "systems engineering." While it is doubtless true "the invention, the design, and the integration of the whole ensemble is actually an old and ever-present part of practical engineering," clearly the conception of "a field of engineering concerned with the integration of the whole as distinct from the design of its parts" is new. Even newer is the activation of this concept by a large profession of systems engineers in a flourishing new industry. It is appropriate that an M.I.T.

Colloquium on parts and wholes should be interested in an engineering field that sets these classic concepts into such novel relationship. The more so as its purpose, in Dr. Ramo's words, is "to optimize the application of science and technology to create a more secure world and a more orderly one that can provide for the needs of the earth's populations."

That the new conception involves more than the conventional administration of scientific labors is indicated by the importance Ramo assigns, early in his paper, to the "multiparameter difficulty." All of us are aware of this difficulty as endemic to scientific study in every field. It is, for example, the critical difficulty that besets every discipline's quest for the "totality" of factors that produce the "ultimate and irreducible distinctiveness" of the whole. The multiplicity of factors, including the noneconomic factors that elude parametric analysis, also leads Kuznets to question whether economics as a separate discipline can deal with its own larger questions. That Ramo includes in his multiparameter difficulty even those "nontechnical" (human) problems that have not yet acquired a parametric identity bespeaks the optimism and the valor of the new systems engineers. Such factors as the "systems engineering team" and the "human subsystem" challenge the parametric imagination.

Dr. Ramo's imagination is not overwhelmed by "the multitude of parameters, the indefiniteness of most of them, and the need for learning to live with probability as a way of life." Indeed, he continues to pose questions as fascinating as, in the present state of our knowledge, they are insoluble. He discusses the need of "analysis for unwanted modes" and illustrates the importance for systems analysis of "nonlinearity concepts." Particularly interesting, in this connection, is the procedure he mentions for stepwise, nonlinear variations in the sampling rate of a quality control system for high-volume operations.

Dr. Ramo's speculations about the future of systems engineering can hardly fail to stimulate fresh consideration of familiar problems. He picks his examples from a field that "will become the greatest growth industry of the next decade or two." This field, for which he proposes the name "intellectronics," will encompass "those systems in which the machines are engaged to a significant degree in intellectual pursuits, relieving man of routine mental effort." By contrast with the dire prophecies of man subjugated by machine—from *Frankenstein* to Orwell's *1984*—this optimistic forecast of machines in the higher service of men is rational and refreshing.

While systems engineers are building this new and higher symbiosis between men and machines, behavioral scientists must continue to wrestle with the complex relations among men. The elusive "human factor," which bedevils economic analysis and complicates systems engineering, is the main business of the behavioral sciences. Theirs is the task of enlarging our knowledge of the whole man while ordering our understanding of the environment—mechanical, social, natural—in which man is but a part. Man's part is indispensable—since he is the dynamic element of the social process, the principal component of the social system—but he is not independent of his environment and cannot be comprehended outside of it.

This is why the behavioral scientist, whose perspective is so lucidly articulated for us in this volume by the late Professor Clyde Kluckhohn, finds himself today in an intellectual situation that is "equivocal." The situation is well represented in the discipline of anthropology, which casts a very wide net by setting human behavior within the context of culture. As Kluckhohn said: "Culture in this sense is a category of a generality comparable to 'gravity' or 'disease'." With so vast a contextual "whole," anthropology further imposes upon itself an extremely complex task with respect to its "parts." Its concern is with "certain regularities or recurrences in human behavior that, *in their totality*, distinguish one human group throughout a specified period of time *from all other human populations* [italics inserted]." It seeks to determine "the ultimate and irreducible distinctiveness of each specific life-way."

This requires a search within each cultural "whole" for repetitive behaviors that involve a selection from two or more alternatives that are physically possible and functionally effective—are "equally open." Anthropology is not concerned with merely biological regularities. That people everywhere eat, sleep, and reproduce is of no great interest until some culturally-derived choice among available ways of performing these functions is regularly discerned. The requirement of "selection from two or more alternatives" seems akin to the situation in which Purcell's little magnets can choose to point up or down—alternatives that are, in principle, "equally open."

But the difference is greater than the similarity. Physicists have sought to simplify the Ising problem of magnetism so that the significant choice—whether or not all the "parts" agree to point in the same direction and thereby form a magnetic "whole"—can be uniquely associated with another unidimensional regularity such as the Curie point of temperature. Anthropologists are not content, however, until all such regularities "in their totality" differentiate the given culture "from all others." Even if one considers the anthropological ambition to be "equivocal," in the sense intended by Kluckhohn, it usually leads anthropologists to conclude that the model of inquiry domesticated in physics can be of only limited utility for them. That such a proposition can lead beyond banal metaphysics to a profound reconsideration of the meaning of culture, and of its scientific study, is demonstrated in the deeply thoughtful essay by the late Clyde Kluckhohn—probably the last analytic exposition of anthropology as a science completed by him, and hence a paper to be read with particular attention.

The final trio of papers form a "set" in an unexpected, and enlightening, way. Each paper, in turn, stimulated the next paper. The process was initiated by Ernest Nagel's brilliant exegesis of the familiar proposition that "the whole is more than the sum of its parts." We reprint the original paper from *Philosophical Studies* in its entirety, for no portion of it is without relevance to the logical roots of our problem. In Nagel's differentiation of ambiguities and articulation of meanings, the reader will find a profoundly valuable guide to some key issues in the contemporary understanding of the ancient problem of parts and wholes.

The impact of Nagel's exposition is evident in the two final papers presented to the Hayden Colloquium, which consider the interaction of parts and wholes in the vast and complex context of language. Professor Roman Jakobson, who recast his final text in the form of a sustained illustration of Nagel's categories, presents an exposition of the advances made by modern linguistics through phonemic analysis of language systems. In this field, as in physics, economics, and systems analysis, modern high-speed computers have made feasible research enterprises that earlier were hardly conceivable. His exposition of language as an object of rational analysis is an implicit challenge to those concerned with man's "subjective" interaction with language. Hence, whereas Jakobson brings us to the verge of aesthetic criteria in language behavior, Professor I. A. Richards, whose paper originated as a comment on Jakobson's lecture, plunges us into the vital center of aesthetic judgment. Under the provocative title "How Does a Poem Know When It Is Finished?" Richards grabs the Pathetic Fallacy firmly by the horns.

Richards commends the organic (more specifically embryonic) analogy to us, not with an apologetic whimper but with an explosive bang. Poems, he tells us, "are living, feeling, knowing *beings* in their own right; the so-called metaphor that treats a poem as organic is not a metaphor, but a literal description. A poem is an activity, seeking to become itself." Only a very narrow-minded positivist would boggle at this defiant assertion before finding out what Richards really is about. He may be cheered by the rather positivist downgrading of biography (as a substitute for aesthetic judgment) on the ground that "biographic speculations as to whatever in a poet's life shaped whatever in a poem must—at present, and very likely, always—have unassignable probabilities."

Richards downgrades the biographical (as well as the historical and even literary) problems "associated with" a poem in order to upgrade the *linguistic* particles that actually form the poetic whole. In a phrase which again reminds us of Purcell's little magnets—looking to their neighbors for clues on how they should behave—Richards defines a poem as "a system of oppositions and collaborations among words." What Richards is driving at—and what finally reveals itself as a profoundly hardheaded approach to the crucial problem of aesthetic valuation—is condensed in one sentence: "In brief a poem begins by creating a linguistic problem whose solution by language will be the attainment of its end."

Illustration of the point is given—perhaps more concisely than nonspecialists might wish—in the comments on particular poems by William Empson and by Richards himself. His intention is clearly to show

> . . . the dependence of what any word or phrase can do in the poem upon what its other words or phrases can do there: the degree of their mutual enablement and mutual control. It is this—not any actions or agonies, any wishes or hopes or endeavors on the part of the poet or his readers—that settles what the poem may be and when and how (and whether) it is finished.

The reader with any interest in the fundamental behavioral problem of aesthetic judgment will be well advised to read Richards attentively. His is a "literary" style of exposition—elliptical, allusive, connotative—rather than the style of a research report. But it will repay the inquisitive rereading of, at first, elusive sentences.

Parts and Wholes in Physics*

EDWARD PURCELL

PHYSICS is surely the place where one expects few surprises as one goes from part to whole. Most exploration in physics is directed the other way, and it has taken us into the domain of the elementary particles, where, at the moment, it seems the deepest questions lie. But, there are interesting and difficult problems in physics which are presented as going from part to whole. It is this family that I would like to review. Indeed, I would like to pose, in the context of physics, the question which I assume this title evokes in all the subjects represented in this series. The question is: Is the behavior of the whole system richer in any essential way than the behavior of its parts?

In biology, perhaps, and certainly in sociology, one may suspect that even when one has unraveled the elementary interactions one will still be a long way from comprehending the life of the system as a whole, and the barrier that remains may or may not be described adequately as one of mathematical complexity only. That is to say, there may be deeper reasons to mistrust analogies between the physics of a many-particle system and a social or biological organism. But I need not face this question for my aim is to make a much weaker point. I want to explore with you one branch of physics where the problem is to understand the behavior of the aggregate in terms of the elementary laws governing its individual parts and where there can be no doubt at all that we are in possession of all the relevant facts about the parts and also about their elementary interactions. Now the surprising thing is that—and this is the only point I want to make this evening—even at this very primitive level, where there is no question of a *new* organizing principle coming in as we proceed from the individual to the system, we find a subtle problem and something very like qualitatively new phenomena.

* This paper was edited from the tape recording of Professor Purcell's lecture to the Hayden Colloquium.

The general problem is one which we call in physics the problem of cooperative phenomena—or, more specially, order-disorder transitions. Some complex systems—complex in the physicist's sense, which merely implies a very large number of particles—can change from a disordered state to one that is orderly, or vice versa. Both of these conditions are properties of the ensemble as a whole, not of the individual. That is, you cannot look at an individual and tell whether it is orderly or not; orderliness implies the *pattern* of the whole arrangement of parts. Still, the behavior of the whole must, in some way, come about from the primitive laws which govern the interaction of the parts. This is a problem best explained by an example. My particular example will be a model in physics that has had a celebrated history. It is simple enough to understand even if you haven't studied any physics for a long time. One can describe it in many ways and it is always, in essence, the same thing.

My example has its origin in the problem of magnetism. When you have a piece of iron which appears magnetic, it does so because all the elementary magnets in the iron, or most of them, point the same way. If they are not almost all pointed the same way, the outside effect is small, and we say the iron is not magnetized. The early theories of magnetism attempted to formulate some picture of what goes on inside iron when the little magnets line up. One of the difficulties was that, at that time, one did not know exactly what the elementary magnets were. But that was not really essential to this problem then, nor is it to our problem now. We know that a magnet consists of a large number of elementary magnets (actually we know nowadays that these are electrons in the iron atoms), which, if they all line up the same way, will cause the whole block of iron to exhibit a magnetic effect. So the question of magnetism is a question of order. The elementary magnets, whether ordered or disordered, are all identical. In the disordered state they are simply pointing in different directions. One of the early and very limited attempts to make a theory of this generated what has become a classic problem in physics, and also in physical chemistry. This problem is named after the man who introduced it in his doctor's thesis in 1924, one Ernest Ising, who published the substance of his thesis in a short paper in the *Zeitschrift für Physik* in

1925. The Ising problem is concerned with a model that might imitate the "cooperative" behavior of the elementary magnets in iron.

If we take a material such as iron, which is capable of being a magnet, and measure the strength of its magnetization at different temperatures, what happens typically is the following. If the iron is very hot, it is not magnetic at all. As we cool it off, there comes a particular temperature (in the case of iron, somewhere below a red heat) where it changes abruptly into a magnetic material. Below this critical temperature (called the "Curie point" after Pierre Curie who performed the early experiments) the elementary magnets in any neighborhood within the metal spontaneously line up with one another so that a large majority point in the same direction. In different regions or "domains" different directions may be chosen so that the specimen as a whole may appear unmagnetized, if it consists of many domains. But this complication need not concern us, for it is the spontaneous ordering of the millions of elementary magnets within one domain that is the nub of the problem. The degree of order is found to increase very rapidly as this material is cooled below its Curie point. At absolute zero, of course, the order becomes complete.

FIGURE 1

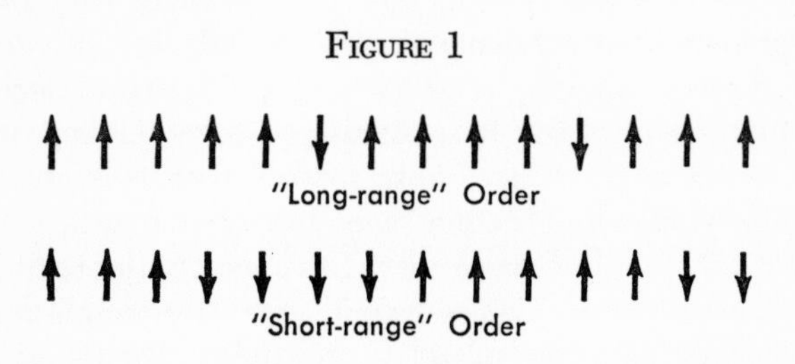

That is the actual behavior of matter. The next thing is strictly a mental construct—a model, the analysis of which is the so-called Ising problem. In the simplest case we have a row of objects each of which has two possible conditions, either pointing up or pointing down (Figure 1).* The nature of the two conditions is actually not

* The figures used in this chapter are from the article by T. Wainwright and B. J. Adler that appeared in the *Supplemento* to *Il Nuovo Cimento,* No. 1, Vol. 9, 1958. They are reproduced with the permission of the publisher.

involved in the puzzle, but we shall identify them as "pointing up" and "pointing down" because we have elementary magnets in mind. The state of this whole chain of elements is described by saying how many are pointing up and how many are pointing down. Now, let us assume that whether a given magnet is pointing down or up, whether it wants to point down or up, depends *only* on what its neighbors are doing. In fact, let me assume that if two neighbors become parallel energy is given off. That is, we shall associate negative energy with a parallel arrangement of two neighbors, positive energy with an opposite or "anti-parallel" arrangement. Thus, pairs that try to get into the lowest energy state will tend to be parallel. In other words, this is a society in which everyone wants to do what everyone else does, but in which each man has a view only of his nearest neighbor on either side. That's all there is to the problem, except for the basic assumptions that temperature has a meaning for this system and that thermodynamics applies to it.

We ask now what, at some given temperature—that is, at some given average energy per particle—is the likely condition of this system. It is clear that if we go to absolute zero, the individuals have to seek the lowest state, and they will all be parallel. But the question is, as we cool the system, but before we get that low, do we reach a point where suddenly there is a fad or a movement that sweeps the whole system, in which a single direction becomes universally popular? Do the individuals get together and say, "Let's all point north; it looks like those fellows over there are pointing north?" The system might thus snap into partial order. Were this to happen, one would have a model that had some relation to the problem of magnetism. This question presents a simple mathematical problem which Ising solved in his thesis. He found that, unfortunately, nothing very interesting happens. When you cool this system down, it gradually acquires more order until finally, at absolute zero, it is fully in order. But nowhere in between does anything sudden happen to the whole community. There is no discontinuity in its behavior.

There are different kinds of order that one can anticipate. If we reach a condition where nearly everyone is pointing up and only a few individuals happen to point down, then we would say we have *long-range* order through the whole chain—if the arrows are up at one end they will also be up at the other end. On the other hand, we can have an order manifested only on a short-range basis; you might find four individuals together pointing down and five together pointing up. This is a highly ordered state compared to a random assembly, but it has no external manifestation because in the physics problem that gave rise to this discussion, these things are only one atomic distance apart, and so there are millions and millions of them in a row. If they are ordered only in this way, we call it *short-range* order. In the case of the one-dimensional Ising chain, it turns out that you can get long-range order only at absolute zero, and magnetism is associated only with long-range order. The kind of order you get before that is just a degree of short-range order.

But this is obviously a far cry from a physical system that has its elements distributed in three dimensions, and the next step is to

FIGURE 2

The Two-dimensional Ising Lattice

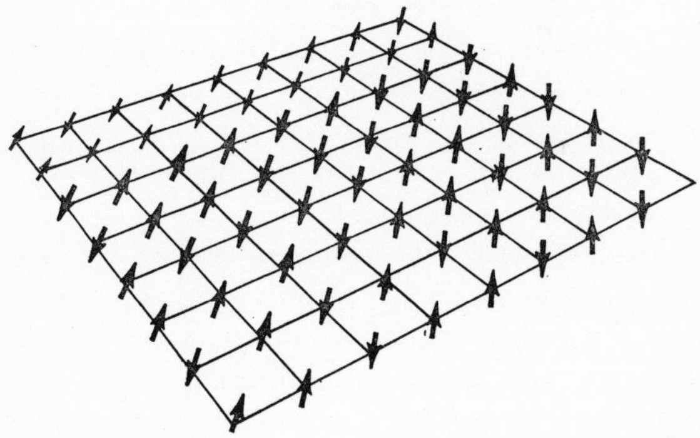

look at a two-dimensional array of things. A two-dimensional Ising lattice has the same elements, but they are distributed on the corners of squares (Figure 2). Imagine the lattice stretching off to infinity in all directions, a sheet of magnets whose individuals can point up or down. The difference is that now each magnet has four neighbors whom it sees and seeks to emulate, rather than two. But it is not the increase in the number of nearest neighbors so much as the new topology of the interconnections that has changed the problem. Assuming that a magnet's preference for up or down depends on its four nearest neighbors only, the question is: does this two-dimensional array behave like a real magnet?

Ising, in his paper, offered a simple and plausible proof that it comes no closer to such behavior than the one-dimensional array. He noted that any time we strengthen the interaction between two magnets it increases their tendency to be parallel. That surely should *promote* the effect we are looking for. Therefore, let us take *all* the interactions crosswise and strengthen them so much that the members of a transverse row all will have to be parallel under any conditions. But now the question of the most likely orientation of the rows as units is simply the one-dimensional problem, already solved, that showed no Curie transition.

Ising remarked that this result unfortunately does not seem to show any of the aspects of ferromagnetism, and on this rather wistful note he took his leave of the problem and the literature. This apparently is the only paper he ever published, and its last conclusion is wrong. Plausible as his argument is and simple as his model is, the conclusion is wrong. Although the one-dimensional chain does not show spontaneous magnetism, the two-dimensional array must do so. This was first proved by the physicist R. E. Peierls in 1936, by a very ingenious argument.

This was the beginning of an assault upon the Ising problem by a long list of very distinguished theoretical physicists and chemists. The history of the problem from then on contains names like that of Kramers, Onsager, and finally, most recently, Yang and Lee. In 1941 Kramers and Wannier found a way to get an appropriate answer in the two-dimensional case and finally in 1944 Professor Onsager of Yale found an exact solution for the thermodynamic properties of the two-dimensional Ising array. It took intellectual troops of this power to crack this problem because the fact is that even the two-dimensional array poses an exceedingly subtle and difficult puzzle. I cannot do justice to the strategy of Onsager's attack but we may look at the result, the predicted behavior of the system as the temperature is changed. Instead of plotting the magnetization, I have plotted the "specific heat," the amount of energy you have to put in to change the temperature by one degree (Figure 3).

FIGURE 3

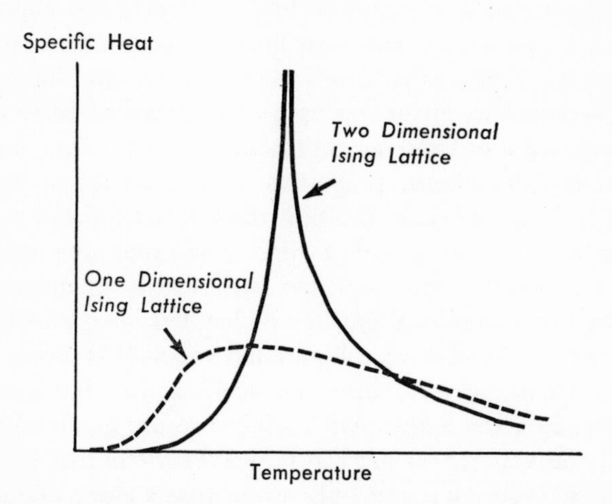

This reflects the changes that are going on in the system. Now we can see what happens in the one-dimensional Ising chain—the row of people who can only see their immediate neighbors on either side—and what happens with the people who can see four neighbors instead of two. The two-dimensional system has a singularity in its specific heat curve. The curve goes to infinity logarithmically, and it is at this point that one has the Curie temperature where order sets in. Indeed, in 1952, Yang produced a formula for the magnetization of this system as it is cooled off, which looks very much like the graph for a real magnetic material (Figure 3).

The main point I want to make here is that in spite of the conceptual simplicity of the model, the behavior of the system is astonishingly subtle. It is not hard to calculate, but also, remarkably, this simple two-dimensional system, as it cools down, abruptly enters a cooperative phase in which long-range order appears. The only physics involved is the assumption that nearest neighbors interact so as to prefer being parallel.

Actually, this model has applications to other things and fits some of them better than it does magnetism. It is a very good model—or rather, the three-dimensional version of it would be a good model—for certain behavior that metal alloys exhibit. If you have an alloy of copper and gold, the question is whether the copper atoms and the gold atoms are arranged in an orderly way in the crystal lattice, or whether they are scrambled. There one finds the same kind of behavior as in the example of magnetism; below a certain temperature, an ordered arrangement prevails. The Ising model can also imitate certain properties of a gas, and a remarkable paper by Yang and Lee in 1952 showed that the condensation of a gas from its vapor, with a very simple model of the gas, can be put into exact correspondence with the Ising model. I think this is the first model of a gas in which it has been possible to calculate the transition between liquid and vapor. It is totally a mental construct. Quantitatively, this is not like any gas, but it is the first model that had the feature with which we are all familiar—when you cool the vapor, you get the liquid. Previous models of a gas, from kinetic theory on, give only a hint that a thing like condensation can happen. This, too, is, in a sense, a transition from a disordered state to an ordered state.

Let me show you quite another approach to problems of molecular order and disorder, a rather direct approach to the behavior of a system of any identical particles. The idea is to look in and find out what the particles are doing—except, again, one uses a model. Suppose we want to know what happens to a dense liquid or gas when molecules are running around bumping one another. Is there anything in this behavior which suggests the onset of long-range order? Well, we know there is in nature. There is *freezing*, in which a liquid changes from a more or less orderly collection of molecules to an orderly one of almost the same density. Somehow, the molecules decide that the time has come for them to arrange themselves in neat, orderly layers and stop knocking one another about in a disorderly way. Yet the forces between the molecules are the same in one case as in the other. No organizing principle enters, other than that expressed in just those forces.

The approach I shall describe has been made possible by the fast computing machines. There are really two different approaches. Each deals with a model that consists of so-called hard spheres. There is a box and the spheres in the box are to be imagined as molecules. The molecules may be pictured as "billiard balls" in the sense that they cannot penetrate one another and each molecule exerts no force on the other unless the two actually collide. This is a very primitive model of a gas, but it has done yeoman service in kinetic theory for a century and is worth trying here. One shortcoming is that there aren't very many molecules in the box. In the example I am going to describe there are only thirty-two.

The idea of Adler and Wainwright, who developed this approach at the Lawrence Laboratory at Livermore, was to follow the actual history of the individual spheres as they fly about hitting one another. The imaginary spheres are started off with some arbitrary directions and speeds. The computing machine follows every sphere, keeping track of it, finding where it hits the next one, where the two go after that, where the first hits another one, and so on. You can see right away why you cannot do this for very many objects. If so few as thirty-two molecules were closely confined by a box, one would expect the walls of the box to influence strongly the configuration of the system. To suppress this influence the walls are "eliminated" by a trick. The computer is instructed to replace any molecule about to bump the north wall by a new molecule *entering* as if through a hole in the south wall. It is fascinating to see the random distribution developing. For example, if you start the system out with all molecules moving at exactly the same speed, after about two collisions per molecule they all have acquired different speeds, distributed in very close agreement with the theoretical distribution curve for an infinite assembly thoroughly randomized.

But this is not yet a cooperative phenomenon; it is just the working out of the statistics of a molecular assembly. Now suppose I squeeze the box down so the molecules do not have room to move. If I squeeze it down far enough, they have to be packed in there,

FIGURE 4 FIGURE 5

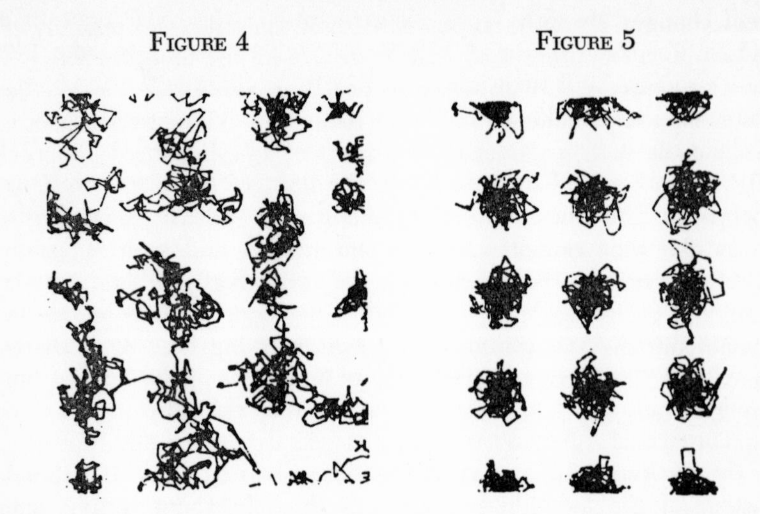

like cannon balls, in some neat way. If I give them a little room, they will presumably jostle around and get a little irregular. What actually happens under *those* conditions? The results of Adler and Wainwright are interesting and surprising. A picture that they published last year shows these molecules as seen from the top of the box (Figure 4). A point of light traces the path of the center of a molecule, showing how it moved in a time during which the whole assembly enjoyed three thousand collisions. Since there are thirty-two molecules, that's roughly one hundred collisions per molecule. One can see that the system is not *completely* disorderly. But although the molecules favor certain positions, they straggle around a good deal.

One can also find a different state of affairs (Figure 5) in which the molecules are well localized; each is vibrating about its home base. So the molecules settle into what looks pretty much like our notion of a crystal—namely, an orderly array. Now the remarkable thing is that these two pictures are taken at exactly the same conditions in respect to relative volume of molecules and free space between them. This is another three thousand collisions worth, merely shown at a different time in the computing cycle. The system changes abruptly from one structure to the other once in a while. For three thousand collisions it will run along looking like one structure, and then it will change to a different average pressure, very much like a liquid changing to a crystal or vice versa. Where the statistics are so difficult to come by, even with an IBM 704 computer, it is a little hard to follow the changeover. Some people at Los Alamos are working with what appears superficially to be the same method, but is actually a different one—the Monte Carlo method—in which they do not follow the molecules in detail, but really do statistical mechanics. They find a similar behavior: at this density, the system will go toward either structure, and it will stay at one solution for a long time; then it will jump to the other solution. Now there is nothing here showing this cooperative behavior but hard spheres of a certain radius.

These hypothetical systems, the Ising model and the hard-sphere gas, teach us that the most elementary interactions can generate, in a large assembly, cooperative behavior the prediction of which challenges our most powerful methods of analysis.

I am not proposing the Ising model as a very deep system. Indeed, I am not particularly interested in it, for our purposes tonight, as a model of physics. I am interested in it as a model of a model because I feel that perhaps it has a bearing on the problem of going from parts to wholes in other situations, indeed, other disciplines. I cannot feel, for example, that the elementary laws that govern an organism, be it a cell or a society, are less subtle than those that govern the Ising model; I am quite sure that anything else one has to deal with is more difficult. Still, we have seen how even this simple system works itself into great complexity when one tries to understand the essential problem of cooperative behavior. I suggest that the astonishing stubbornness of the Ising problem stands as a sober warning to anyone who attempts to carve a path of rigorous deduction from the part to the whole.

DISCUSSION

Parts and Wholes in Physics*

Q. It seems to me that something funny is happening in physics at the moment, especially in high-energy physics, where we are spending vast amounts of money and electronic effort to create conditions that we will never encounter in order to investigate what happens under these conditions. In a way, our interest in physics, after all, is to understand the world around us. We have been pursuing very successfully, for fifty years certainly, the point of view that if you can go after the building blocks—the elementary pieces—and pursue them further and further into the more and more microscopic, somehow it is going to get simpler. And this is why we're doing it. Basically, we think that somehow there is an elementary building block that will help us understand the world in which we live. What is happening is that graduate students will not deal with anything below ten Billion Electron Volts because it is not fundamental enough. I am wondering where the definition of fundamental lies, in the face of the kind of thing you're saying. Do you share my suspicion that we may be approaching a turning-point—in which we consider as fundamental, perhaps, the point at which these microscopic views link with the cooperative phenomena, that is, with the world around us? Perhaps I said this too obliquely.

PURCELL: My view, as a physicist, is that there is probably nothing here that's very fundamental, in the sense that if it were given to one to solve all these mathematical problems, one wouldn't be any wiser as a physicist for solving them. But it is only a model for a question in another field where the answer might not be so trivial. But whether there is anything like this at a different level —this is a question I don't even feel secure in guessing about. I don't even know what it means.

Q: Then you believe we are looking, not for new phenomena

* Because of the extensive interchange of opinion among the Questioners, some have been identified by a number to facilitate following the discussion and the references of the participants to one another.

(I think we are agreed that are no new phenomena), but for new insights, which will make this a much easier kind of problem? Do you really think that, basically, we can either take a physical approach or one of extremely complex mathematics?

PURCELL: The invention of a new way of going at this problem, which exposed its basic behavior without making such a long chain of mathematical manipulation, would certainly be an intellectual treatment that would make everybody happy. But I don't see any problem of the same type in the other domain or—as you go deeper in the direction the graduate students are going—I don't think this kind of problem is going to be found there.

Q: I meant, do you think the interest in physics is likely to shape in a generation, ten years from now, to this kind of problem—the problem of micromolecules, for example.

PURCELL: I'm sure there will be people interested in this problem. The question is whether the center of physics will shift to this interest. There's a very interesting case of this with the one-dimensional problem. This has come up with the work of Dottier on the Helix coil transition in a long chain, which, on the face of it, seems to violate a fundamental theorem about the one-dimensional system. No doubt, this area of micromolecules is going to be very important, as you can see in the *Journal of Chemical Physics* right now.

Q: Are there other examples of this sudden transition? As I understand it, the shift from a gel to a sol would be a movement from order to disorder, and from a sol to gel would be a movement from disorder to order in columns.

PURCELL: Yes, it's the same sort of thing.

Q: Are there types of transitions of that order other than the magnetic ones?

PURCELL: In a sense, freezing is one, and the change in alloys is another. The molecular example I mentioned is one in which you have a long molecular chain in solution that rather abruptly (not with mathematical abruptness) makes a change from an ordered chain.

Q: Is that what's called polarization?

PURCELL: No, polarization is a linking together of molecules.

This is simply a change in the configuration of a molecule, a change in the arrangement.

Q: Would you include superfluidity or superconductivity, or are they on the border?

PURCELL: I'm not sure how one would defend including them. This is not a quantum effect; it would happen also in a system that had many ways to point. In fact, there is another model—the so-called spherical model—that also displays a Curie point.

Q: Do you equate order with whole and disorder with parts?

PURCELL: Order and disorder are, in this context, only properties of the whole. The part is only a featureless atom. One can only judge the order, just as one can only judge whether letterpress type is ordered by changing the position of one letter. You have to look at the whole thing and see if there's a pattern.

Q: So many cases of "parts" are artificially induced by fractionation or analysis. You don't get them in actual experience till you break them down.

PURCELL: The parts we're talking about here are the ultimate atoms or molecules, which, in this situation, can be regarded as indivisible and immutable. The only thing they can do is occupy different positions or stand in some different geometrical relationship to their neighbors. This is not a chemical reaction.

Q: That was my question—whether it was more than arrangement of parts.

PURCELL: It's nothing more than arrangement, and the orderliness that sets in is strictly a geometrical orderliness. Now, the reasons for it are, of course, energetic reasons. The system is energetically biased toward being parallel. We have other states of order. In magnetism there is the interesting one called antiferromagnetism in which the molecules are biased just the other way. If one is up, the neighbor wants to be down. In this case the ordered state is when they are up-down, up-down, all the way through. That comes about by changing the sign of the preference.

Q: Would such a simple-minded example as road traffic be relevant? It makes quite a difference whether the cars follow the rule of the road, sticking to their own side, or whether there's some sort of a random attempt. This gets to be really a problem at a traffic circle.

PURCELL: In this situation, you have natural selection working. When does this situation arise? In the simplest form, it arises in a system of many parts when what one part does is dependent on what the others are doing, where the preference of one depends on what the others have chosen. Whenever this situation arises, one has the possibility of this kind of responsive behavior.

Q: I believe that there have been some analyses of situations like the road problem and they show, theoretically, certain effects known as saturation when you get more than a certain amount of traffic.

PURCELL: You have a maximum flow on a road, which you get when you start a shock wave, if you have traffic traveling too fast and too close together. It's a little different problem—a dynamic one. If one car stops, the other cars all jam on their brakes. This sends down the stream what is kinetically equivalent to a shock wave. You can't get any more cars per hour over the road than you can at that point.

Q: I tried to read that metals article in *Superfluid* and it spoke about metal aggregates. Would this have anything to do with that? The author used aggregates of momentum.

PURCELL: Suppose we talk not about the positions of the objects but about their velocities. They must form a pattern of velocities, too, and that's the kind of thing that comes up in superfluidity. That would be an ordering with regard to velocities rather than positions, an equally valid case of an ordered assembly. In that case everybody wants to be on the move, going in the same direction as his neighbors. So you get an orderly migration in which there's no jostling, because they all have the same intention—the intention being generated, however, by the individual's neighbors. That's the crucial thing.

Q: There's an interesting loophole (I hope there aren't any lawyers present because I might be wrong) in the legal distinction between contract and tort. As I understand it, in a contractual relation, within a framework of order that's always present, you have no constant expectations of the other party except in terms of what has been contracted. The rule of the road, on the other hand, is a beautiful example of tort relationship. If you're driving on the road, you have a right to have everybody else observe the rules, so, if the other fellow is driving negligently and endangers you, you can collect from him. You don't have to know him, it's a completely impersonal situation. If, under specified conditions, he violates expectations, then there's intervention to try to correct the balance. Whereas in the contractual relation, there's no intervention unless there's a particular relation to a unit of agreement that has been specified in advance. These are two different levels of order. Do they have any physical analogies?

PURCELL: I don't know. I'm deeply suspicious of all physical analogies, and that's really the point of my talk. For example, some people have attempted to draw analogies between demographic behavior and simple physical laws, that is, inverse squares of population density, or something like this. My own feeling is that any resemblance there must be regarded with deep suspicion. The behavior of anything as complex as a thousand people is probably more complicated and subtle than the Ising problem. The fact that physics made out very well with kinetic theory, which enabled one to predict averages of pressure in a million molecules, is no indication that you will be able to use successfully the same techniques to the same depth when you're dealing with a relationship involving human interaction.

Q: I think the analogy here was meant on a different point. There are two situations, one in which the order is established because there is constant interaction, as in a compound, which would correspond to the contract; in the other case, the order is established even though the interaction occurs only rarely, namely, where there are collisions, which more nearly corresponds to the tort. They are not arranged in an orderly fashion, because they are constantly in contact. That would be the cannon ball packing you mentioned, and this is not what exists here. If the question were—is there a variety of principles that establish order?—I think you would want to answer yes.

PURCELL: Yes. A rather trivial example is that if I impose a magnetic field externally, I can force the parts to line up—each one obeys the imposed law and disregards his neighbors because the law is stronger. That would be a "contractual situation," so to speak.

Q: You might project this question for a second. The model you showed, in a box of a certain size, is a sample of a total community, and you have to assume that it's big enough so that you have some predictability. Are there any examples in physics of sampling in different ways from those used in social science? You may reject this as a crazy question, but it seems to me that their method is quite different than the method of sampling you described.

PURCELL: It's true the community is limited. One is exploiting here what's obvious—the assumption that things don't change with time in any fundamental way. So, if I follow this box of thirty-two molecules for ten thousand collisions, it's true that I have only thirty-two molecules, but I will get an enormous number of samples of the ways in which they might behave. In physics, we're always interchanging a time average and a population average, exploiting this to the hilt, as in the example I gave. As a matter of fact, experimenters have also studied larger numbers of molecules to see if they would agree, at least in a limited way. They more or less did—enough to give one confidence that thirty-two is a large enough number.

Q: Of course, in doing so, you're making an assumption. You're going from the whole to the semi-whole, which you might call a certain set of parts, down to the final individual. To a certain extent, you are assuming that there is some relevance in going up from a part to a whole, provided the part isn't too small.

PURCELL: That's right. It isn't obvious when you start that thirty-two is a large number. It might have some peculiar features—

Q: It could conceivably be any number?

PURCELL: From the mathematical point of view, no finite lattice in any number of dimensions can have a Curie point. The singularity that comes in here is very much a feature of going to infinity.

Q: You took this model of the Ising problem, and you showed that you could derive from the individual characteristics of the model the heat capacity versus temperature, or the magnetism, or the Curie point. If I understand what you've done, you've implied that from the part, you can derive the behavior of the whole. You also pointed out that, even if it appeared to be a simple case, going from the part to the whole is extremely complex and, thus, one cannot expect to be too successful or successful too often. One of the things that interests me is, do you mean to imply that the behavior of the whole can be totally inferred from its parts, and if so, why do you feel this way?

PURCELL: In this situation, I have the moral conviction that it can, because I have the moral conviction that one knows everything about the parts. This is only a conviction. I don't know how to prove it. There isn't anything else here but us molecules, so to speak. The rest is all mathematics. Whether one can make the same type of statement about other types of systems—whether one can about society—is a question that I specifically beg. I don't know. It seems to be an open question.

Q: Do you think it's an open question in biology?

PURCELL: No, I really don't.

Q: Could we push that naively? Is this because we don't know the parts? You more or less assume that we know all about the parts and therefore we can predict the whole. In other fields, isn't it the lack of knowledge about the parts that prevents us from predicting the whole—even prevents us from having the philosophical feeling that we could eventually predict? Do we have to know the parts well in order to predict the parts; or even if we did know the parts, would we still not understand the behavior of the whole?

PURCELL: My weak theorem is not very helpful. That is, even if you know the behavior of the parts, and even if there isn't anything else, you're going to have a very difficult time. But a much more important question is whether you must be prepared for essentially new laws to come in. As far as biology is concerned, I have a feeling in my bones that you don't know anything more.

Then there comes the question of time. Suppose it turned out that it took 10^{77} calculations to solve one problem. You might be able to sit down and prove that with all the molecules in the universe arranged in the corner of the computer, it would take more than the life of the sun in our sequence to solve this problem. Then it's a question of whether you want to call that problem soluble or not. You can easily generate numbers of that size. The great intellectual feat is to reduce 10^{77} to 10^{7}.

Q: Then your computing is already represented by an analog computer which is itself, in this case, so you wouldn't have to use all the elements in the universe to get the answer.

PURCELL: If you want to try it and see what it does, then you raise the question of whether what it does is different from what it would do in an ensemble universe. Does history repeat itself, and so on? History is an entirely different problem, one that is nonlinear and has all sorts of gimmicks in it that don't appear in physics. I believe we are in the horseshoe-nail period of history.

Q: Isn't there another point of semantic confusion? You say you know all about the parts; but you also know something besides this. You've got some principles of interaction. They're extreme principles of interaction in this case; nevertheless, you can't solve this problem at all without the law that a fellow wants to behave in a certain way in respect to his neighbors.

PURCELL: I mean I know all about the parts plus their elementary interaction.

Q: Now, can we take that one point further and suggest that knowledge of parts hardly exists without knowledge of elementary interaction? In other words, we can't conceptually isolate parts without knowing the context in which parts are placed. If the behavior of one of your thirty-two particles really depended intimately on the behavior of all the other thirty-one, then is there any sense semantically in saying this is the problem of the part that hit the whole? The concept of the particle is a special kind of abstraction and no empirical unit has ever been just a particle.

PURCELL: I think you've put your finger on another hidden assumption in physics. We're used to dealing with two-particle interactions. When we get stuck, as we do in the nucleus, and find that this isn't enough, then things get complicated very fast. In my example, there are two-particle interactions. You've just described a case in which you have thirty-two-particle interactions and that would be quite a different matter. Unless you want to talk about the narrow problem of finding the most stable configuration which is—

Q: But, in a sense, it is the most stable configuration. One finds out whether the configuration is the most stable under certain pressure-temperature conditions.

PURCELL: Well, suppose you did the same thing for the gas and the liquid. You might be able to do a theory for each that found their internal energy and showed there was a difference. But you still haven't got a description for the phase of transition.

Q-1: We have been able to compute the total energy of both phases as they varied with temperature in such a way that they crossed at right angles at the lowest energy state.

Q-2: But you didn't have this kind of a problem computed in your distance function, where you had all these different configurations to worry about.

Q-1: No, it's more restricted.

Q-3: And then, too, the interaction's much more complicated.

Q-2: I want to go further and ask, do we know any parts, or are they all inferences from the behavior of the whole? In a society, we can say the individuals are parts and the society is the whole. But outside of that, are there any parts that we can point to and name, except by inference, that are constituents wihin a whole that operates in certain fashions that physics has been very ingenious to discover? I just wonder if we're not dealing with artifacts.

PURCELL: In physics, one has a special situation in which the notion of identity of parts is a sharp one. If there are thirty-two helium atoms in this box, what a physicist means when he says those are identical parts is something very strong. Let me take just one kind of isotope—just Helium 4, say. These things really are identical in a fundamental sense, which you infer from the totality of their behavior. You just don't have that advantage when you're dealing with things that are complicated when you look inside them.

Q-1: Isn't this a function of a system of order in which what you identify as the significant properties of these units is some kind of an abstraction in respect to the system in which you see it? I think of the social analogy in terms of money. Money is a system of social order of a very special sort. You can say that from the point of view of the producers of the commodity, all purchases of units of that commodity at unit price are interchangeable. Now we know that the human beings who are these purchasers are far from interchangeable in hundreds of other respects. But with respect to being willing to pay five dollars per unit for a particular commodity, they're identical. Isn't there possibly that sort of a conception?

PURCELL: The helium atoms really are interchangeable. That's what we mean by identity. If they weren't, we'd call it by a different name.

Q-1: My point is that this is a function of the system of order in which they're placed.

(*Everyone talks at once.*)

Q-2: It's the essence of quantum mechanics.

Q-3: That's just the last fifty years of physics.

Q-4: You spoke of the identity of the particles; then you spoke of the interaction. Isn't the interaction a statement about the whole, so that really you're not inferring the behavior of the whole from the particles? Rather, by stating the interaction, which is a statement about the whole, you're deriving properties of the parts from properties of the whole. Or is this just a semantic problem?

Q-1: If you have a situation where several systems of the same parts can exist within the whole, then your problem is to infer from the part to the various types of systems that could be created from it. It seems to me that the properties of the parts you're concerned with would derive from the whole. This is, in short, the kind of problem we deal with in social science when we talk about economic systems, social systems, and political systems. These different kinds of system involve different attributes of the same part. Whether it's relevant depends on what system you're dealing with, and you have a lot of complications here. But it seems to me that your problem is not too clear. To what extent are you working from the whole to the part in defining your parts?

PURCELL: Not very much. I think less than you would in almost any other situation, because we can take these atoms off by themselves and do other things with them, in fact almost one at a time. It's true that our confidence in our deduction is based on the success of this whole body of theory—some of which looks at many particles, and some of which looks at one. But I think that, peculiarly in this physics, you have a grip on a single part and its interaction with another part in ways that you obviously hope to have in any—

Q: You have an even stronger case here in the sense that what you're doing is a mathematical problem by definition. Your particle has these properties—

PURCELL: . . . with certain rules. It's funny that you can make a game with simple rules, yet such a subtle game.

Q: But that's exactly the point. It's all very happy for us, ever since the Renaissance, to believe that we each have great unique qualities as individuals. To come down to fundamentals, maybe we're not unique. I submit to you that, in physics, the things you're interested in about these particles are identical. There are other things you're not interested in that might not be identical, but they don't matter to your problem.

PURCELL: Identity has some very deep consequences. It is not an identity only in the sense that it doesn't matter which one that you take. This is, of course, the great difference in the quantum way of thinking on the microscopic level—that this identity has consequences that go beyond saying it doesn't matter which one you pick.

Q-1: And yet, if, for example, all protons were exactly alike except that there was a variation of one part in 10^{20} in their mass, but otherwise, everything was just the same, there would be gross things in the specific heat of molecular hydrogen that were just completely different.

Q-2: But why do little particles that don't want to conform line up when they reach a certain temperature?

Q-1: You cannot know which one does and which one does not.

Q-3: Then why is this a theoretical problem? This is what baffles me. Take the one-dimensional case. You have two choices for each particle—up or down. Then you have three possible wholes or patterns—long-range order, short-range order, and some disorder pattern. Why isn't this just an empirical problem, to find out the temperature at which each of these occurs?

PURCELL: Because there are far more than three possibilities. That's the trouble. The way in which they can be arranged and still have the same numbers of like neighbors is astronomical. You have to find a way to count them. In other words, those two examples of different kinds of order are chosen out of an enormous range of possibilities, each of which would look different in detail, but would have the same general features. So you have the problem of abstracting—of asking only the questions about a particle that describe it in its class rather than as an individual. Suppose you want to know where each molecule is. You don't know what state the system is in until you can give the up-down for every molecule in a big telephone book—so huge a number of possibilities that you can't even write it down. You have to find some way of classifying them that will reproduce the over-all properties of the whole thing. That's what this kind of statistical mechanics is. You'd be very happy if you could do that with any other of your problems. You could predict what fraction of people would do so and so. This would be enough for you to consider that you had solved it.

Q: But doesn't the theoretical problem arise where you want to distinguish the class, so that it stands out from all other classes? Doesn't that just require finding one of the cutting points on the statistical continuum?

PURCELL: No, you have the intermediate case, because below the Curie point you have a certain fractional relationship between the particles. The majority of them will be up, and there will be a certain number down. You want to know what that fraction is. You don't care which ones they are because they are identical anyway. That's the type of solution one is looking for in this sort of problem.

Q: Is this what Weisskopf said in last year's Colloquium [on *Evidence and Inference*] when he said that mathematics is not about the particles but about our knowledge of the particles?

PURCELL: You can make that remark apply to physics.

Q: There are two problems here. One is particular particles and the other is statistical aggregates, where you don't care which individuals fall into which statistical class. All you're interested in is the distribution by statistical classes.

PURCELL: These theories have a hard time predicting in great detail. If you have a square array in some kind of ordered state, there's no guarantee that the spins that are down don't spell out Pepsi Cola. You'd have a terrible time pulling that out of the theory.

You'd probably never know whether that kind of order prevails without finding some way to count the number of ways of spelling Pepsi Cola against the number of ways of spelling something else. So you're more modest. You ask questions about the average number up and the average number down, and that's the best you can do.

Q: May I go back to a previous question? I gather you would be content if it turns out that the human body and its behavior could be computed in finite time from electrons and nuclei. I mean that wouldn't be a big surprise to you.

PURCELL: Finite time? It would be a surprise, because you can so easily generate superastronomical exponents.

Q: But your lesson is an optimistic one. Namely, if you take a piece of iron and look at it in three-dimensional configuration, it's more or less a lattice with a lot of irregularities and more or less identical atoms with a fair number of impurities and isotopes—all mixed up, a problem of tremendous complexity. And yet, you say, I will now make a model in which I will try to distill some of the essence of this complexity, if I'm lucky. This model consists of each iron atom seeing only its closest neighbor, just on a two-dimensional array. Now I'm clever enough to do the arithmetic. Then, the tremendous surprise is that the essence of magnetism comes out of this great simplification of this tremendously complicated piece of iron. You're pointing at an optimistic moral—at least for physical systems—which is that their essence is not contained in complexity, but in simple aspects that you know how to pick out. You don't have to do this computation with molecules in the body to find out what makes the body function.

PURCELL: It's a triumph like the triumph of kinetic theory, but more hard won from the present point of view.

Q: But aren't you underestimating the stroke of genius in spotting the key thing, that each one does what its neighbor wants—that this is really the key? There were a lot of other things you could have said about the individual particles. But this was the relevant feature of the part in terms of the kind of whole you want to deal with. Now, if you could find the same relevant part in the individual and deal through him with the whole society, how wonderful it would be. Here you slide over what is really the stroke of genius.

PURCELL: The theory of magnetism that preceded this—the so-called phenomenological theory of Weiss—had the idea that what one does depends on what the others are doing. He said, "The way I will represent that most simply is to say that what one does depends on the average of what all the others are doing." That makes a very simple theory which gives an astonishingly good picture of these laws. But there was some dissatisfaction with that theory—because you know that one spin a centimeter away from another can't really care what the other is doing; that its only way of knowing, so to speak, is by the grapevine from one neighbor to the next. Therefore, you try to make a more realistic picture in which messages are only transmitted from one neighbor to the next. This is more realistic because we know something about the nature of physical interactions—that they aren't long range—and the new picture takes account of this. That was what Ising was attempting to do. He saw quite correctly that the essence of his innovation was to draw a model in which only short-range interactions were involved, as we knew they had to be, in the physical system. If you have to give credit to anyone at this point, it probably comes earlier, give it to Weiss for the concept of how to make this primitive picture of co-operative action.

Q: Yes, but you could have conceived of every third neighbor—or something like that. There are so many possibilities here.

PURCELL: It's pretty much the indicated simplification. Every third one would be unlikely. In actual practice, it's probably the nearest neighbors and the next nearest neighbors, but that's obviously much more complicated. Next nearest neighbors have been done in one-dimensional chain, but—

Q: Can a distinction be made between order and organization? As I take it, you've been talking about different types of order—serial, linear, and so on. Can we make a distinction between that order and what we would call organization in organisms and social institutions? There the problem of part and whole becomes a much more difficult one, and one that we're still struggling with.

PURCELL: There seems to be an enormous quantitative distinction; whether there is a qualitative distinction, I don't know.

Q: I feel the same about the jump you made from your disorderly to the orderly. It's a somewhat analogous state.

PURCELL: What would you call organization as opposed to order? Could it manifest anything that you would dignify with the name organization?

Q: I don't know. That's what I'm asking you.

PURCELL: You speak of organization when you see something which, in some sense, has a purpose. I don't mean metaphysical purpose.

Q: I take it in Wiener's sense of feedbacks. Then organisms and social organizations show purposive behavior in his sense. I was just thinking whether there was another order or class of events that you would call organization as distinguished from order?

PURCELL: Suppose you take helix coil transmission—that is sort of verging on it. Here's the long molecule that is going around every which way. Then it decides, along with all its neighbors, to get into a nicely organized spiral. That's a kind of organization. It may have a "purpose" in the sense that, in the new configuration, it can do things it couldn't do before. The step from that to a molecule so arranged that it can start grabbing parts and reproducing itself may not be more than a quantitative step.

Q: But in organization, as I understand it, you always have some kind of differentiation. Before anything can be organized, there must be differences and some kind of communication system. One simple analogy would be a football team. Each of the eleven men learns to assume a certain part and, by the way they communicate and interact constantly, they create the team. What happens is that they are then governed by the team that they themselves have created. This gives rise to something quite different from mechanical order because it involves a circular, reciprocal relationship.

PURCELL: I think this is present here, really. This team has a very simple objective in life—to be pointed all in the same way. That's organization.

Q: Where does the differentiation come in?

PURCELL: You can imagine a system where you mix in different components, and perhaps it will separate into phases with different concentrations. You then have what you might call two teams, one pointing one way and one the other. As in any ferromagnetism, they choose up sides and their pole is determined by the team they land on.

Q: The difficulty lies in the fact that what you consider the relevant part of the behavior of the football team is probably—from the physicist's point of view on these things, even if we refine and refine—completely irrelevant. There's a minute difference, I think, in terms of the kind of organization we are talking about. This is just a peripheral detail, which I don't think we'll ever approach because your question is so different from the kind of question that we ask. From our point of view, you're asking an absurd question. It's a little bit like how to spell Pepsi Cola.

Q: Might I suggest what seems to me a borderline case of a combination of ordering and organization? It occurs in all biological populations of bisexual reproduction with a certain kind of order in types of human populations—namely, adult households—that is, simply an ordering of pairs. But there are two prior organizing principles also at work. The whole population prior to the ordering by pairs is somehow sorted into two basic categories—male and female. And the focus of the household is one of each of these two categories, not any two at random from the total population. This is a terrific phenomenon of order in our society. Over ninety per cent of those of marriageable age live in marital households.

PURCELL: The physical analog of this is a frivolous one that doesn't have this subtlety at all, namely, a chemical reaction which forms a diatonic molecule with an ionic bond. It's chlorine and hydrogen united to form HCl, but you have molecules of H, Cl, and HCl all over the place. That is much simpler to describe in these terms because it is just a two-by-two business.

Q-1: That involves differentiating only when you get those particular pairings and this curious phenomena of offspring.

Q-2: And only when you get this particular combination of HCl do you get spectra that are characteristic of HCl.

Q-3: Simple as this thing is, I think it has something more in it.

Q-4: I think the difference is that it matters what question we don't ask. We can make hydrochloric acid, but we cannot make hydrochloric acid in which one particular proton goes with a particular chlorine atom. That matters.

Q-5: You spoke about close interactions in this organization-order thing. Now, in organization you're dealing with interactions through communication. I just wondered whether the distance (travel) and the kind of communication (that is, length of communication) would be another distinguishing characteristic between your type of order and organization.

PURCELL: I don't think the distinction is how far apart they are or by what means they communicate. Here, essentially, the communication is only between a limited group. No one molecule can sample the whole affair and decide what it's going to do. That would be going back to the old Weiss theory intact. It can only decide by what its neighbors do, and they only decide from where their neighbors are. In fact, the difference between the one-, two-, and three-dimensional problems here is a topological difference. In the one-dimensional system, this neighbor has this neighbor and this neighbor; whereas, in two dimensions, you can close a loop. In three dimensions, you have the problem that lines and space don't close (as I understand it from just casual reading in the subject). This is part of the mathematical difficulty of the three-dimensional case. It's purely a topological difficulty in the structure of the communication network.

Q: Could you plot either circular or cyclical structures?

PURCELL: It wouldn't be so easy to plot them in geometrical space, but you would still have some sort of topology of the communication lines by which this preference is felt. It's clear from these examples that the nature of the problem will depend very much on the structure of that topology.

Q: The pituitary communicates, let's say, with the ovary by sending a hormone message, to which the ovary responds by sending a message to the pituitary when another phase comes. So, you've got a reciprocal message at a distance.

PURCELL: You have the same thing here. One of the molecules in the array communicates to the second; the second communicates to the third; the third communicates to the fourth; and the fourth one back to the first again.

Q: I wonder if it isn't different because the pituitary FHl, when it is poured into the blood stream, doesn't have a specific target. It's a message, which is selected out by the ovaries because that is the only receiver with a concern for that particular message.

PURCELL: It just means that you have a different circuit diagram on the map, but I don't think it makes any essential difference.

Q: But you have selective communication content. All communications aren't the same. Isn't this an important difference?

PURCELL: Yes. That's a little more—

Q: He could put this into his model except that life would get much more complicated, and then he wouldn't be able to solve it.

Q: As Wiener said, you send the message "to whom it may concern." But in an organization, there's always somebody with a concern for one of those messages. Is there in your model?

PURCELL: Yes. Your neighbors are always concerned with whether you're up or down. You can put in next nearest neighbors; it doesn't change anything here in any important way, as long as you have some limited number of neighbors.

Q: You could have a problem more difficult to solve. Let us say you have each one communicate with its mirror image on the opposite side of the array.

PURCELL: Actually, that's what you do in antiferromagnetism. It's called superexchange and there is just that model. But the point I want to make is that the circuit diagram—or the connections—define the problem in this primitive sense. And I think that would be true also in the much more complicated cases you're talking about.

Q: There's no problem about the recipient of the message having to decode it as there is in organization.

PURCELL: No, but I don't think that's an essential complication. A decodable message is a message. An undecodable message is no message. In a lot of cases there's no message, so I think it's the same thing logically.

Parts and Wholes in Economics

SIMON KUZNETS

I. *Wholes*

IN THE PRESENT DISCUSSION, I define "wholes" in economics as units that we study in the hope of understanding and, if possible, predicting their responses to different conditions. The variety of such units, depending upon the principles of internal organization, major function, size, and complexity, makes it difficult to set up a classification that is widely acceptable. The one below is of necessity only tentative.

"Decision units" are those within which decisions, with respect to the function performed, are concentrated in some single hand, although they may be affected by the pulls and pressures of all the members of the unit, that is, by the parts of that whole. Such units range from individual members of economic society to more complex units—producing firms, households, nonprofit associations, elementary government cells; to associations of individuals, households, or firms—workers' unions, trade associations, farmers' alliances and the like (each of which belongs to the category so long as it manifests a unity of decision with respect to the function that it performs); and finally to the nation-state. The latter is clearly a complex whole within which decisions of major importance that set the conditions for economic activity are made: on rights of property in land and other chattels, on freedom of association for defense of group interests, on internal improvements, on freedom of movement of goods and people across the boundaries or within the country, on taxes and disbursement, and so on.

The reason for defining and identifying such wholes or units is obvious. If a locus of decision with respect to economic matters can be discerned, the framework of that locus must become a unit in economic study: it is at that point that the analysis of factors affecting the decision must be concentrated.

"Group units" are aggregates of decision units with identical or similar function (or other similar economic characteristics)—firms belonging to the same industry, workers of the same occupational status, households of the same demographic type and economic level, and nation-states at similar stages of industrial development. Thus we can group all firms producing shoes into the shoe industry and deal with that industry as a whole, on the assumption that identity of product means similarity in technological problems, market position, and other relevant conditions vis-à-vis firms in another group, say the steel industry. The group unit called "the shoe industry" is distinct from the decision unit called "the trade association of shoe manufacturers." Likewise, we can group all wage earners in all firms and speak of them as "labor," distinguishing them from other individuals within the firms and from the material capital employed in them. Here, too, the group whole called "labor employed in the shoe industry" is not the decision unit called "the shoe workers' trade-union." Finally, we can view nation-states with similar bases and patterns of economic operation as belonging to a group called "industrialized nations," but this again must not be confused with a decision unit that industrialized nations may join for the performance of some common task.

The group whole, characterized by similarity of function, not by unity of decision, is distinguished either for the sake of simple expediency in aggregation or for the purpose of analyzing the changing role or structure of the group as a whole by careful study of the divergent behavior of the individual decision units within it. In the light of these purposes, it is clear that the similarity need not be with respect to economic function only: it may also be with respect to size, legal structure, or any other characteristic that uniformly affects the economic behavior of the decision units included.

"Exchange units" are congeries of decision units (from as few as two on upward) tied through the exchange of the economic goods or claims that they produce or possess—whether the exchange is primitive barter, a free business market, or a system subject to rigid planning by some central authority. These wholes, which can for simplicity be called markets, range widely in the type and variety of economic goods covered, in the character of decision units linked, and in the rules governing the exchange. That the analysis of such market or exchange units is central to economic study need hardly be argued; and neither the decision nor the group wholes, as defined above, coincide with them. The distinctive characteristic of these wholes is the linkage of their constituent parts through markets—not their "togetherness" because of similarity of function or some other important economic characteristic, or the *unity* of decision (for it takes more than one unit to engender a market or exchange linkage).

Although these three types of wholes or units do not constitute an exhaustive classification, they are sufficient to suggest the range of wholes distinguished in economic study. The comments that follow are in the way of additional reflections on this classification:

(1) Clearly, the complexity within each type varies widely. Decision units vary from the individual member of society to the nation-state, and for some functions, an association of the latter. Group units vary from a narrow whole like the boilermakers in the X industry in Wisconsin to a wide one like the proletariat of the world; or from the billiard table manufacturing industry of Switzerland to the group of industrialized nation-states that account for more than half the world's total production. Exchange units may range from the apple market in a village to the world-wide petroleum market; from the competitive market among small firms to the oligopolistic markets of industrial giants; and so on.

(2) The wholes or units are defined in *relation* to certain criteria, and not necessarily identifiable by overt characteristics. Thus, a business firm is a decision unit with respect to the major economic function that it performs, for instance, the production of shoes; it is at the same time a framework within which one or more group wholes operate, for example, all wage earners employed by it; and it is also part of several market wholes. A more complex social unit, like a nation-state, is a decision unit with respect to some functions, a group whole with respect to some characteristics, and a market entity with respect to linkages among constituent decision units within it.

(3) Obviously, a recognizable entity—an individual, a firm, an association, and so on—can at one and the same time be part of a number of decision units, group units, and markets. Consequently, directly observable, institutionally identifiable entities cannot coincide with strictly defined decision, group, or market units of any given type.

(4) It follows from (2) and (3) that the wholes are artificial species of "ideal types" created to facilitate economic study. This wide variety—the possible cross-combinations of decision units, group wholes, and market units can lead to overpoweringly large numbers—is a product partly of the range of functions that can be studied and problems that can be examined, and partly of the range of institutional responses to changing conditions of economic reality.

(5) One obvious indication of the variety of wholes in economics is the extent of specialization in the discipline. It includes agricultural economists and industrial economists, monetary and banking specialists and specialists in transportation, economists who deal largely with domestic commerce and those who specialize in international trade; and, in addition to all these and many other kinds of specialists, there are the groups concerned with the more general aspects: economic theory, micro- and macro-, and economic history, detailed and descriptive or comparative and generalizing. They are all involved in economics—the study of social relations that have grown around the activity related to the satisfaction of wants that demand scarce resources. The very existence of a specialty means that a particular group of economists views the institution or process being studied as a "whole" whose parts are to be distinguished so that the behavior of the whole can be properly analyzed without continuous reference to the relation of this particular institution or process to a still wider whole of which it is a part and within whose framework it must operate. So many specialties mean, therefore, at least as many wholes.

This proliferation of specialties is a product of the inventiveness of human beings in evolving institutions, that is, social complexes of established patterns of behavior, in response to the changing conditions of economic activity. Thus, with the multiplication of money and financial institutions, the need for money and banking specialists developed, since it takes years of application to learn the rules and response patterns of these institutions and of the groups in society affected by them. And the same need was felt in other sectors of productive activity: the governmental sector vis-à-vis the private sector, foreign trade and other foreign flows compared with domestic, and so on. Each of these institutions, each of these wholes, has distinctive rules and responses; none of them can be interpreted adequately on the basis of any one pattern—conceived by introspection—of human responses throughout the range of economic activity. Each must be studied on its own, as a whole whose behavior is to be observed and explained. The list of wholes must, therefore, be long and varied if it is to reflect the complexity and proliferation of distinct institutions in the numerous sectors and at the various levels of economic activity; and the choice of the whole depends on the problem that the economic analyst wishes to study.

II. *Parts*

The nature of parts in economic study has been already implied in the discussion in the preceding section. If we start with the nation-state as the largest and most complex decision unit and ask what parts, that is, what entities *within* the space and time coordinates of a nation-state should be distinguished, the answer is simple. The units narrower in scope than the nation-state all constitute a wide variety of parts. Thus, we can distinguish different industrial sectors among the nation's producing firms, different groups among the men engaged in production, different groups of households, and so on.

The multiplicity and variety of distinguishable parts is naturally reduced as we move down to the narrower and less complex decision units. But even in the individual firm and in the single household, component parts are usually distinguished. If only because these firms and households involve more than one individual and usually call for a stock of material wealth, they are comprised of such distinct parts as labor and capital, or consumers and consumer wealth.

Even in the case of the individual member of society, the primary decision unit, we may and should distinguish parts. In fact, the individual is treated in much economic analysis as a possessor of specific resources geared to the output of a specific product. The parts are the potential resources of the individual as a producer (either of his own services or as controller of the services of his capital) and his potential wants as a consumer.

The parts within a group whole may be either the primary decision units included, taken singly or grouped into some meaningful subcategories, or, if the group is treated as a single aggregate, that is, as a single decision unit, the parts may be distinguished by analogy with a decision unit—a practice justified by descriptive convenience but hardly by analytical relevance. Thus, within an industry one may distinguish every individual firm and observe its operations, deriving from their interaction the behavior of the industry as a group; or one may deal with subgroups of firms—large and small, young and old, and so on—all in aggregative terms.

The parts within a market or exchange whole are implied in the definition. The simplest exchange unit consists of two decision units, one on the supply side and the other on the demand side, both defined with reference to a single good. Beyond the simplest to the most complex whole there is a wide range in the number of decision units (or groups of them) and in the goods involved in the exchange links.

Further illustrations, which easily come to mind, are superfluous. Obviously, parts, like wholes, are subject to a wide range; are not coincident with existing entities—individuals, firms, industries, and so on; and are constructs designed for analysis. This becomes clear as we deal with two broad questions: (1) Why and how do we distinguish parts? (2) How are these parts combined in the whole?

(1) The first question can be answered easily in general terms, although the specific answer in a specific situation may require a long cumulation of tested information. The general answer is that we recognize parts whenever some entity within the whole appears to be different from the rest of that whole, either because it has some special relation to the human beings participating in economic

activity, or is subject to some special technological constraints, or is so distinctive in other ways that we may expect its pattern of behavior to be different from that of the other parts of the whole. The usual presumption of analysis is that the entity within the whole, so distinguished, may be related to factors different from those affecting the other parts of the whole; and that, consequently, the segregation of the part would maximize the prospects of establishing some stable connections.

To use a simple example, in studying a country's economy we distinguish agriculture and manufacturing as separate parts because we recognize the difference in the patterns of the production process as well as in the long-term elasticities of demand for the products, and hope to understand the processes of the economic growth of a nation better if we study agriculture and manufacturing separately than if we merge the two. The rationale for distinguishing parts is thus simply that the observable differences among them promise greater success in analysis and in the reduction of a disorderly reality to a simple structure of relatively stable relations. But the selection of the specific parts that will reveal analytically significant differences is a problem in itself—because the choice is guided by existing knowledge and the hypotheses that it generates. And, since current knowledge is incomplete, we may overlook important parts and distinctions. To illustrate, we do not distinguish within national products, or within a group unit like the shoe industry, the parts comprised of firms with managers or entrepreneurs whose names start with A, B, C, and so on down the alphabet; and the reason is that we do not expect that the differences that would emerge from this distinction would help us to understand and explain economic behavior in general or the movements of national product or shoe output in particular. But do we expect that the age of entrepreneurs and their personality structure would be significant factors, and if so within what range? The main point is that the distinction of parts in economic study, when it is not mechanical, frivolous, or pandering to journalistic desires to identify some notorious groups, is for the purpose of better analysis, explanation, and generalization of the behavior of the whole; and thus depends upon the state of our knowledge, changing and varying with this knowledge.[1]

(2) But the parts are parts of a whole, and must therefore be related to each other. How are they related, and how are they brought into this relationship? The answer depends partly upon the nature of the whole, and we begin with decision units, and take the single producing firm as an example. We argued above that its distinctive characteristic is unity of decision on important economic questions (what to produce, how to produce it, what prices to ask, and so on). It is the entrepreneur, individually or in committee, who brings together the parts—the various grades of labor and the types of capital needed for effective production. The relation among these parts is complementary, in the sense that they are all needed, and each depends on the others' presence if it is to serve the basic function of the whole. They are brought together in a business firm in a free society through the private markets in which labor and capital offer their services, and in an authoritarian society they may be conscripted by ukase. But the relation among these parts within the firm, while truly complementary with respect to performance of the productive function, becomes a bargaining one when it comes to either the conditions of such performance or the division of the net income originated in the firm—the difference between the value of product and the cost of purchases from other firms—with employed labor, employed capital, and the entrepreneur contending

[1] Perhaps these comments give an idealistic view of why parts are distinguished in economic study and discussion. In fact, different types of activity and different positions within a firm give rise to group interests, so that one may speak of the interests of farmers, workers, property owners, and so on; and the same may be said of inhabitants of one region of a country versus those of the others. Many group interests do not necessarily have an economic base, although eventually they may produce economic differences. The existence of group community of interest and consciousness of belonging to a distinct group may induce observation and study of economic aspects, whether or not such distinction serves truly analytical purposes. To be sure, group cohesion is likely to have economic effects, and thus, in and of itself, may provide an analytical basis for distinction. But it is also true that much untestable ideology is generated in the service of group interests and aspirations; and much economic writing is concerned either with elaborating distinctions that serve a particular group ideology but are not geared to objective and empirically testable propositions, or with refutation of such ideological exercises.

for shares in this net product. The unity of decision within the firm is essential precisely because the cooperation required by the complementary relation of parts in the performance of the function must be assured in the face of latent conflict about conditions of participation and the sharing of the product.

What we have said about the units called firms could, with wide modification, be extended to households, whose major function within the economic sphere is to decide on the use of income. The parts, in this case the individuals within the household and their wants, are held together by family ties rather than by the market or legal compulsion nexus; but there is complementarity among the members and the wants, and there is conflict in the sense of pressure of the parts upon the limited magnitude of the whole. But we may be stretching the analogy, since the economic calculus of the business firm and of the free market is not truly applicable to family life or, in fact, to the activities of many other noneconomic institutions, for instance, the church.

On the other hand, the analogy can be extended to a whole like a nation-state in which the decisions made by the sovereign agencies of society govern the conditions under which industries, nationwide labor and capital, or groups of nonprofit associations complement each other in order to provide—under socially desirable conditions—the wide variety of goods that enter the national product. The mechanism involved may be the private markets, markets restricted by government regulation, or some prescribed plans of an authoritative and usually authoritarian central agency. And yet, given the necessary complementarity of industries (defined broadly) and of labor and capital, there is also conflict among them either in respect to conditions of operation or division of product. Here again, unity of national decision is required to assure the necessary cooperation in the face of latent conflict.

Complementarity in function and latent conflict in bargaining for conditions of cooperation may be found also among parts of a group unit—when the latter is treated aggregatively as if it is a decision unit. One can thus talk of cooperation and conflict between labor and capital in the shoe industry. But the dangers of such aggregations, which disregard the existence of such basic decision units as individual firms, groups of workers, and so on, within the industry, are obvious enough—in the sense that failure to distinguish them would make it difficult to explain an industry's behavior. Among the discrete decision units within such a group whole, whether taken singly or in some meaningful subgroups, complementarity and collaboration do not operate in the sense in which they do between labor and capital within a firm or among different industries within a country. The prevailing relations are those of imitation and competition—imitation in that the decision units within the group learn from each other and competition in that they vie with each other either for resources, or for markets, or for both. It is this process of imitation and competition, which may prevail not only in a free market society but even in an authoritarian society (with its "socialist" competition), that is important because the distinction of parts related through these processes sheds much light on the behavior of the group whole.

The relation of parts within the market wholes or units is obvious: it is one of competition when the parts are on the same side of the supply-demand equation, or one of bargaining when they are on opposite sides. There is no cooperation except through the bargain or exchange, and there is no imitation, unless we define the congeries of decision units on either the supply or the demand side of a market as a group whole just because of such location.

III. *Uses*

To distinguish a set of wholes and parts within each whole does not carry us far in explaining economic behavior, even if we know that the parts are related to each other in cooperation, imitation, competition, and bargaining. We need some general knowledge concerning the "drives," the principles of operation, of these parts and wholes and concerning the characteristic conditions under which the parts cooperate, compete, and bargain. Indeed, economics, even at its most abstract level, includes a number of quasi-empirical generalizations on these topics, although they are often presented as formal assumptions with no immediate claim to empirical validity. Yet the fact that these particular assumptions are made is in itself an indication of reference to observable reality.

Such general assumptions as maximization of profit by the firm, of income or welfare by the individual, and of total product by the nation, are empirically based assumptions, in the sense that each may be claimed as the most realistic *single* principle of operation of the decision-making units involved. The law of diminishing returns, or of proportionality of factors, is an inference from the complementarity of various parts operating within one set of technological conditions, while the law of increasing returns is a generalization suitable for a different set of conditions—and examples of both either as historical tendencies or as experimental functions can be found in observable reality. The principle of diminishing utility has an empirical content directly derivable from the limitation of human desires for any specific good, and is, in a sense, an inference from the complementarity of desires, broadly defined, for individual human beings under certain often-found conditions.

It is impossible to discuss in detail the combination of generally assumed principles of economic activity, and broad generalizations concerning technological constraints on it, with the delimitation of the parts and the wholes that has been suggested in the preceding two sections. All I want to do here is to call attention to this combination in economics: decision units, group wholes, market units, and the parts distinguished within them, are activated with the help of broadly assumed principles of action within some empirically constrained conditions of operation. It is the introduction of these principles of action and conditions of operation that converts the distinction of parts and wholes into a working system; and, as already indicated, the very definitions of wholes and of parts are affected by whatever we postulate or know about the criteria of action or conditions of operation.

The performance of the resulting model and the problems upon which it will shed light naturally depend upon the principles and conditions of action assumed—with the distinction of parts and definition of wholes governed accordingly. It may thus be a model for analyzing the impact of short-term changes in taxes on small firms in a given industry or of long-term changes on the various sectors of a nation's economy. Or it may be a model for analyzing the impact of a given type of wage policy on the economic growth of an industry, or a nation. And so on.

Such models, simulacra of economic reality, have many uses; but one fundamental application runs through the history of the discipline. It is concerned with the relation between the individual and society, the part that is in itself the primary unit and the complex social whole that dominates its individual members. Since economics is by definition a study of social relations, this interplay between the individual and society is necessarily its essential concern. The ever-present intellectual puzzle that confronts economic study is how to explain the social result in terms of individual actions. And the purpose of the long chain of connections, which runs from the individual to the firm to the industry to the region to the nation, and so on, or from the individual to his economic class to the nation, and other varieties of grouping and linking, is the better specification and analysis of the relation between the two termini of the chain.

One aspect of the way this basic task is resolved in economics should be noted. Clearly, there is no individual outside the framework of society, nor is there any society except as it is reflected in the patterns of behavior of its individual members. To conceive the task of explaining the social process as the result of individual actions—as if one could start with "nonsocial" individuals as the primary units, each a *tabula rasa,* and end up with a social result—is obviously to deal with what in essence is an insoluble assignment. And indeed, despite the impression that may be conveyed in some economic writing by references to Robinson Crusoe, no such fruitless task is ever attempted. Instead, the individual units are endowed with principles of action and conditions of operation that are already a product of the social framework within which the individuals operate, even if the assumptions thus made contain a far more generalized and hence less complicated formulation of *socially* conditioned patterns of behavior and of *socially* determined conditions of operation than a more realistic description would require. Thus, the maximization principles are not truly descriptions of innate and inescapable characteristics of human "nature" to be found regardless of the kind of society in which individuals operate. It is hardly an accident that economic theory and analysis, as we know them, evolved largely during the historical periods and in the societies in which the assumed principles and conditions of individual behavior bore some resemblance to the way the individual members of those societies operated in those historical times.

IV. *Difficulties*

The obvious point above must be emphasized since it is here that many of the inherent difficulties of erecting a structure of parts and wholes, which in combination with assumed principles and conditions of operation would provide a valid theory of economic processes, emerge most clearly. For it is exceedingly difficult to subsume the numerous institutional links in the *changing* chain that connects individual actions and social results under a set of simple generalizations, particularly in terms of a few principles or conditions of economic activity proper.

Let me illustrate the difficulty by reference to the complex unit that we call the nation-state. One obvious thesis of economic analysis has been that the cooperation of individuals within society, their combination as parts in a social whole, produces far greater results than would be secured by the same individuals working in isolation. Adam Smith, the founder of the discipline, began with the proposition that the nation's income is a function of the labor devoted to its production, and the productivity of such labor is in turn positively associated with the extent of free division and specialization of labor, and so on. It follows from these elementary propositions that the wider the division of labor, the wider the collaboration of complementary parts, the greater the excess product of the whole over the hypothetical output of the component parts operating in isolation. And, strictly speaking, one should infer further that the larger the whole, the larger the nation-state, the more room within it for cooperation of complementary parts, wider division of labor, and so on; and if for some reason nation-states must remain independent of each other, free movement of goods and resources among them should in the long run benefit all concerned. Yet the world has paid only scanty tribute to such inferences; and, what is worse from the standpoint of the relevance of economics to some major problems, economic analysis per se cannot define the factors that make for a nation-state, that determine when and why a given group of X individuals or households will form a wider complex that will then make important decisions for channeling and governing economic and other activity.

One can speculate on the reasons for the world's refusal to accept the inference of greater advantage to the parts, the human beings, either of organization into wider state units or of free intercourse among the latter; and it is these reasons that suggest the limits of analysis within the discipline of economics. Productivity of labor is not a function only, or even largely, of the wider division of labor; another major factor in labor productivity is changing technology. Changes in technology that have resulted from scientific discovery in modern times and have accumulated into what might be called a stock of "potential productivity" can be tapped by a group of individuals organized into a social whole only if measures are taken to provide the capital investment needed to embody the new technology, the skilled labor needed to man it, and the social conditions necessary for the new technology to operate at a tolerable level of efficiency—unhampered by family nepotism, government corruption, obsolete property rights, and so on. All these measures require some sacrifices, and, at the first stage, acceptance by social and economic groups whose *relative* (if not necessarily absolute) social and economic position will be diminished by them. Social decisions that mean a decline in the relative position of some groups, even if beneficial in the long run to the majority of individual members of society, can be imposed by a sovereign state only if there is sufficient consensus, sufficient consciousness of kind within the group, to support the decisions. For example, it might be easier for ten million Phrygians (to use a fictitious name), who, by dint of historical heritage, feel a community with each other, to accept a decision by their sovereign government that, by disfavoring some and favoring others, can accelerate adoption of modern technology and thus economic growth, than for these ten million combined with twenty million Sydonians to do so—if, because of different historical heritages, the two groups are not willing to accept a single, active, sovereign government. It is thus possible that expansion of the nation-state unit, if it weakens the coordinating power of the state, will *not* lead to increased economic productivity. Similarly, one could argue that the free movement of resources and goods among nations is not necessarily an assurance of greater economic growth of some of the partners if the added risk of new technology must be paid for by protection from the competition of the more advanced among the national units.

The comments clearly indicate that imputation of income maximization or class interest to the individual units in deriving the connection between their individual behavior and the social results omits an important element (in this case the existence of a national community) not incorporated into the structure of economic analysis. To put it differently, noneconomic elements are quite important in the formation of units employed in economic analysis and reflecting observable reality; and this is only natural because very few of the units whose decisions have a major effect on economic activity are purely economically oriented and determined. Even business firms may contain a number of noneconomic elements. And what is true of the units is true of parts: there are no purely economic classes, or clean-cut productive factors. But it is the noneconomic elements in the decision-making units, in the bases on which parts cooperate, that are of major interest here, for it is the cooperation and complementarity of these parts in the decision unit that is of the essence in economic analysis and in the "whole being larger than the sum of its parts." Of most importance is the fact that in the larger and complex unit, like the nation-state, the noneconomic element that forms the base for cooperation overshadows the elements susceptible of economic analysis. Granted that we can measure the economic results of cooperation within such a unit and some aspects of its structure, our analytical tools are not adequate for explaining their formation and their capacity to provide conditions for economic growth or other desirable patterns of economic behavior. We face here a fundamental question of whether economics as a separate discipline can deal with the economic behavior of such larger units—a question that can perhaps be paralleled by one concerning the usefulness of economics in dealing with the household unit, also much affected by major noneconomic considerations. But this means that in its structure of wholes and of parts, and its assumed conditions and principles of operation, economics deals with only a part of the economic process, with only a part of the social relations that have grown up about the production of material means for satisfying wants, and sometimes not the most important but only the most analyzable parts.

Even in the treatment of topics that are within the purview of economics proper, two difficult aspects remain. The first, already stressed, is the choice of the parts that may or should be distinguished within a complex whole—the problem of disaggregation. It is possible, on the one hand, to conceive and analyze the behavior of a social whole as a single gigantic market in which the individual units collaborate and compete without grouping the latter into parts distinguishable by peculiarities of response and behavior (except as to their position on the total demand and total supply curve); and, on the other hand, it may be desirable, if difficult, to distinguish scores of different groups and markets, even though all are interlocked. The more aggregative treatment can reveal nation-wide forces and factors that would elude us in the detailed treatment, unless the latter is comprehensive and lends itself to thorough summary; but the detailed treatment can convey much more about the *mechanism* by which the global, aggregative results are produced.

Obviously, a combination of the aggregative treatment with the maximum meaningful detail within the aggregates is analytically most productive. But since data and intellectual resources are scarce, some choices must be made, and the ways in which such choices are made in economic study vary greatly. Moreover, the choices are often affected by the pressure to secure the most defensible answer to an acute problem or question of policy, and these problems and questions change, if not from year to year, from decade to decade, and from generation to generation, and they may well differ among countries, with obvious effects on economic study within each. This does not mean that continuity and cumulation, or comparability among countries, in the parts and wholes structure of economic study is completely lacking—especially when the data are quantitative and susceptible to fruitful cumulation over time and effective comparability in space. But it does mean that since full coverage of parts and wholes is not feasible, the emphasis of much of the qualitative and some of the quantitative analysis in economics shifts from time to time and differs from country to country.

Finally, there is the problem of change over time. Neither the behavior of economic units nor the structure of their parts is static. The technological conditions of economic production change; the groupings of producers shift boundaries; the sets of values that guide consumers and producers shift; and so on. All these changes over time could be handled in the structure of parts and wholes if one could establish invariant patterns and thus conceive the complex units as results of the interaction not of fixed parts, with fixed principles of behavior and under set conditions of activity, but of parts that change systematically in weight, acting on principles subject to systematic and known changes, and under conditions that are subject to forecastable trends. Since the time of the grand, dynamic generalizations of the Classical and Marxian schools, which, because they were so oversimplified, were proved wrong in almost every respect by actual trends, we have not established tested growth patterns in the discipline of economics; and we are groping for them now under conditions that promise only a few valid generalizations. Yet we must learn something about these patterns of change over time and at the same time be able, in our analysis, to assume some basic conditions and principles sufficiently constant to permit derivation of determinate and defensible results, at least for the short run. Much of economic study is in fact devoted to these two, somewhat dissimilar tasks: learning enough about the patterns of change over time in the economic wholes and their distinct parts to be aware at least of their magnitude and the general direction of their trends, and analyzing the relation between the parts and the whole under assumptions of constancy of some basic conditions that would permit determinate and useful analysis, even if only for short-run problems. While there is an obvious connection between the two, one must admit that even the definitions of some parts may necessarily differ between the two sets of problems; and the results of some short-term analysis may be quite misleading if transferred bodily to the study of long-term changes. The relevance of these comments is that the variety of parts and wholes in economic study results partly from the difference between emphasis on long-term change and emphasis on short-term problems. This is, in a sense, an elaboration of the general theme that choice of problem affects definitions of parts and wholes, but the cleavage between the two complexes of problems just indicated—of growth and of valuation and current allocation of resources—is sufficiently important to deserve special mention.

DISCUSSION

Parts and Wholes in Economics*

Q-1: Do you distinguish, as they do in biology, between associations that are simply aggregated, as a flock of birds, and associations that become dependent on each other, as in a hive of bees—with its workers, its drones, its queens, and so on? Do you make a firm distinction between association and an interwoven, integrated, and interfixed organic relationship?

KUZNETS: I make a distinction involving a group aggregate. This is not organic, since it shows an interrelationship of parts only in the senses that I mentioned—competition and imitation. Now, I don't know enough about flocks of birds. But if the flocks of birds have a leader, who usually heads the array, and a fixed order of procedure, which indicates some division of labor, I would say that this is more like a decision unit. The flock is more like a firm.

Q-1: You see, this may be so in geese, but not in crows. These things get very subtle after a while.

KUZNETS: I don't see what the problem is. It's either there or it isn't.

Q-1: All I'm saying is—take an industry. You say it's an as-

* Because of the extensive interchange of opinion among the Questioners, some have been identified by a number to facilitate following the discussion and the references of the participants to one another.

sociation. But the minute the industry begins to gang up on the public—

KUZNETS: Well, with respect to the industry ganging up on Congress and the public, it's a decision unit. A trade-union is a decision unit, in a sense, on the questions that the trade-union decides upon. But an individual worker can compete with another worker in many respects. The individual worker is still a decision unit who transfers some of his decision responsibility to the union.

Q-1: But, in other words, everything's both, or can be both.

KUZNETS: It can be both. In other words, industry, as a trade association, is a decision unit, and industry, as a collection of individual firms, is a group aggregate.

Q-2: I want to ask whether you haven't played down the group aggregate too much. That is, you've implied that the decision units are those that act, but you consider industry as acting as a unit only through the trade association. I would argue that, in economic analysis, industry pays a good deal of attention to its interaction and responds to certain restricted sets of common situations, so that you have things like representative firms, which are nothing but a picture of an industry.

The justification of this is, as much of what you say implies, the much closer experience the firms have within an industry, compared with what they share with different industries So, there is a sense in which we would treat industry as an organic entity, even though we recognize that decisions are made within the individual firms, but, in order to explain what has happened in an individual firm, you have to take account of what has happened to the other firms in the industry as well.

KUZNETS: My answer to that would be that there is no law against, nor is there any crime in, an analyst treating a group aggregate as if it were a decision unit if he does it for analytical convenience. But if you ask how an industry responds to, say, rising cost, the real answer lies actually in the decision of the individual unit. The mechanism of response is diverse. Smaller firms respond in a certain way, bigger firms respond in other ways. The different structure of cost and so on, in each type of firm, is an important explanation of how an industry responds. You see, I am very suspicious—although I should be the last one to say that, having worked with these aggregates all my life—I am very suspicious of basing an analysis upon the reaction of one aggregate to another without, somehow, having a picture in one's mind. How does, say, manufacturing industry respond to a changed market situation? Or how does agriculture respond to the changed technological conditions accompanying industrialization? To my mind, one difficulty with much of the analysis in the field I'm familiar with, economic growth, is that the neglect of that mechanism—that is, neglect of the group aggregate as a collective decision unit—a conversion of it to a kind of representative firm—omits some very intriguing and important problems.

Now, let me give you an illustration: Here was agriculture in the United States with a per capita income per worker lower than the urban per capita income in any real terms for decades. Why didn't the returns equalize a long time ago? Why weren't there enough people moving out of agriculture to equalize the returns? That question can be answered only by asking: who are the units? how many of them are there? in what position can they move? And you see, this change, this very striking reduction in the proportion of the labor force engaged in agriculture, while it is accepted by everybody as a generalization so common, so obvious, is still, in fact, not explained properly. Nor will it be until we treat agriculture as a collection of decision units and study their responses to the conditions that are reflected in the movements of these aggregate totals, or averages. And that's all I was stressing.

Q-3: Might we move a little toward the edge of economics to entertain our colleagues here from other fields a bit? You said that one problem was that the specialist in any given field of economics finds that the general principles aren't as applicable as they seem to be because, you said, he knows the coefficients, whereas the general theorists do not. Now I suggest another reason why he finds they aren't applicable, and I'd like to ask what you think about these two reasons relative to each other. It seems to me that he doesn't find them so applicable because, as soon as he looks hard at a particular field, he finds that a lot of the behavior there can be explained only by taking as variables some noneconomic factors that the economic theorist takes as given. If he is studying, let us say, labor, when he sits down to explain the relations of management to labor, he has to take into account some noneconomic business. If he's studying agriculture, and is really going to explain this lag in moving out of agriculture, he promptly introduces variables that aren't economic. So I would suggest that the difficulty is that he starts turning "parameters," noneconomic givens, into variables, and that this is a greater difficulty in that he has coefficients that the general theorist doesn't.

KUZNETS: My reply to this question is that I hope that you're right, because that would be very hopeful, if it were true. If I were to open a book on labor economics or on trade-unions, and found a decent account of "noneconomic variables," noneconomic givens converted into actually handled variables, I would be delighted. But I'm not sure that there is such a case.

Q-3: Let me clarify. I would not want to assert that the economic specialist does this well, but I would want to assert that the reason the general economic principles aren't so applicable is that he's aware that there are some other things that he does not understand. While he has been trained primarily in economics, he is aware of the need for considering noneconomic factors.

KUZNETS: Let me answer again by saying I don't think the statement should be that the economic principles are not applicable. The statement should be that they're not interesting: they're too general; they don't give you the important result. It isn't enough to know the general shape of the function; you've got to know much more than that; and in order to know much more than that, you've got to know a great deal about this particular set of conditions. In the old days, when there used to be interest in business cycles (maybe there's still interest), there was conflict between the people who wrote unitary, general business cycle theories—deriving some sort of cyclical model either from unitaries or from the acceleration principle, and so on—and the people who were studying separately, say, the behavior of a speculative type of business, or of producers' goods. The latter were studying the actual peculiarities of the behavior of sufficiently different, sensitive groups.

Q-4: It seems to me that these are arguments and not questions.

I also have an argument, and I have to start with "three platitudes," referring back to our problem of the whole and the part. First, platitude number one: what is a "whole" and a "part"? or, what is a "quality" and what is a "quantity"? These are relative terms, which may shift when two phenomena, A and B, are compared with respect to them. One may be a whole and one may be a part; one may be quality and one may be quantity. The same one that is quality may become quantity in a relationship between B and C.

KUZNETS: This is all one platitude, you say?

Q-4: This is the first one, yes. The second platitude is our problem of explaining the wholes in terms of the parts—for example, individuals. And platitude number three is only a variation of number two, translating it. We ask ourselves where, for explanation's sake, we can apply partial differentiation to either one variable or several, because partial differentiation precisely explains the whole in terms of its parts. I submit now, coming back to economics, that the real problem is that—taking whatever different decision units you select, the household or the firm—methodological individualism broke down. It couldn't explain the whole in terms of its parts—namely, the decisions made by single decision units—not only because the decision units had noneconomic motives of behavior and conduct, but for other reasons also.

There are inherent reasons why methodological individualism, or the attempt at explaining the whole in terms of decisions by the parts, will break down. For instance, consider imperfect markets. Where there are indivisibilities, where the normal partial derivatives do not determine the maximum, they also do not determine action. The means that, in any effort to make single decision units explain the behavior of the whole, there are certain inherent difficulties beyond the endogenous factors. Our problem is to see where statements of methodological individualism are insufficient, where we have to complement observation of single decision units by certain additional statements about the whole and where only both together can give us a determinate solution and either one alone cannot.

KUZNETS: What do you have in mind besides, say, indivisibilities and certain technical facilities?

Q-5: I wonder whether indivisibilities are really a case in point because that means only that the individual unit, which you otherwise would have selected, is just not suitable for the particular case. For example, a part of a railroad is not good enough for anything because it doesn't lead anywhere. It is the whole that brings the part into our general consideration—our economic calculus. So, indivisibility as such, I think, has nothing very much to do with the problem of parts and wholes as such, but only with the kind of parts we are going to choose. This is precisely how Dr. Kuznets stated the point.

Q-6: Then, it really isn't necessary to beat things over the head with this indivisibility business. I would go on to say [Questioner 4] doesn't need indivisibilities for his theory. Let's take one of the simplest classical problems. Let's have a world of no indivisibilities —pure competitional order, let's say. It would still be to the advantage of one nation out of the complex of nations to act as a monopoly. In other words, it's not just imperfect markets that are facts of life. The inherent breakdown in the individualistic logic is that it pays to create imperfections in the market where none were before.

KUZNETS: Would that statement be defensible in the long run?

Q-6: I am sure it would—to a restricted group. If they all play the game against one another, you're back in self-defeating behavior.

Q-7: But, even if they don't—if you have some measure of welfare over the whole universe?

Q-6: You make it trivial. It becomes one decision-making unit.

Q-7: That's right. Optimizing consistently.

Q-6: But this is a real denial of the market because it says you have to have the whole world turned into a single administrative unit. And where's the market then?

Q-8: But, all you're saying is that there are certain cases in which it doesn't pay to talk about parts, so we talk about the wholes. If the monopoly is a whole, we talk about wholes. There are no parts. That's all there is to it—very simple.

Q-6: What you're saying, essentially, is that even if you limited all problems of noneconomic motivation and even if you maintained the problem in its classical economic form, and whatever you decide to call a part, the fact remains that we do not have a determinate solution. We cannot say things qualitatively about the response of the system, even in direction, to a change in one of these variables. It's only under very special assumptions about technology and taste—never mind about what's noneconomic—that we can say anything at all about the response of the system to a specified change in technology or anything else. There are whole varieties of things, normally taken to be very much a part of the same universe of discourse, that break down the determinacy of what we can say. This is true even without introducing any concern about households that aren't interested in maximizing satisfaction or firms that aren't impressed with maximizing profit. I'm skeptical of the view we've heard—that, within the universe economists consider their own, we've sort of solved all relevant problems, and what we've really got to worry about is that this isn't really a relevant universe.

Q-9: But aren't you just shifting your ground? Aren't you just saying that some problems are more soluble than others?

Q-10: I would agree with that proposition.

Q-6: But that has nothing specifically to do with the problem we're discussing here—the problem of parts and wholes.

Q-10: Quite possible.

Kuznets: I may agree with you and I agree with [Questioner 6] but somehow it doesn't loom that important in my mind. Let me be quite outspoken. I don't agree with a lot of the refined writing on welfare economics. Also, I don't agree with the postulate of noncompatibility—I mean, the impossibility of interpersonal comparison. This is the kind of refinement in the pure logic of economic analysis that has nothing to do with real problems. In real life you do make personal comparisons, and you base yourself on them, and a lot of policy decisions are based on them. The technical exigencies of getting a determinate solution under these very refined conditions don't bother me so much in economics. I'm willing to put aside the refinements and say, let's return to primitive economics. In a sense, within the economic sphere, it's good enough for our purposes. What's missing is what the economists have gradually removed from economics as "noneconomic" variables—population movements, political structure, everything that, in terms of the kind of problems that beset us today, involves the most important factors. This is an expression of my own personal judgment. Now I agree with [Questioner 6] in the sense that you can get these types of compounds and not dissolve them into logical individualism. But the question is: How important are they in terms of the impact of economic analysis on the conception of problems?

Q-11: If my interest were in grand prediction, surely I would agree with you. But what I would say is, let's not throw out much more narrow, much more limited problems. I refer to such problems, for example, as production optimization, and decision mix of investment, over the next five years in an Indian context. There, it seems to me, an awful lot of narrowly technical economic problems that we haven't managed to deal with are very real problems. We haven't solved them and they're highly relevant and useful to economics.

Q-12: A good many people think the size of the exogenous shock is very significant. A small shock will be absorbed by individuals, and the aggregate won't react to it specifically. A large shock may produce a political shift, causing an aggregate unit to act in some political, noneconomic way. I'm impressed by the fact that, when the price of wheat falls in Europe, the British bow down, a million workers as individuals, and the French merely coagulate to take political action. No economist could predict which is going to do what.

Kuznets: What is your answer?

Q-1: I think it's a very close thing whether you have an aggregate of individuals or an organic unit. I think that this is a tricky problem—whether this flock of birds is going to act as a unit or as an aggregate—or disaggregate from time to time without thinking about it.

Kuznets: I didn't mean to deny that this is a tricky problem. But the problem is that there's a difference. Your illustration seems to suggest that there is no difference.

Q-1: There's an important difference in the economic response, but there's a very difficult problem in distinguishing in the economic data how this difference is going to come about.

Q-6: The problem of creative response—that's the thing you are talking about. We can go on to say that adaptive response is possible and can be predicted, but the creative response cannot be predicted, only explained. Is that what you're talking about?

Q-13: I would add to the list of responses, suicide.

KUZNETS: I don't know if state action in this case is a creative response. It's also an adaptive response—in one case by the state and in the other case—

Q-6: Well, more than that. Can you perform a sufficient amount of refinement on some two dollar maple sugar? I think you can convert it into the equivalent of ten cent cane sugar. And, I suspect that you agree that we have done a similar operation on refining economics.

KUZNETS: Analogies are very dangerous.

Q-14: There's a question I've always wanted to ask you, and this is the occasion, I guess.

KUZNETS: Does it have anything to do with the talk here?

Q-14: It turns out to have something to do with the subject. Why is it, despite your work on these highly disaggregated sectors and unique contributions to the study of retardation sectors, that you made a jump to the aggregate study of national income—to these broad aggregates—and have never linked this work with your book on secular trends and the work on national economics?

KUZNETS: In fact, I did link it up. As you look at my book, you will find that there is much relationship between the analysis of impact of the retardation and movements in the different production centers on the aggregate.

Q-2: I'm a little curious about Gerschenkron saying the kind of problem that has been raised several times is just a question of picking the units. What do you mean?

GERSCHENKRON: Exactly what I said. First, we have a frequent but compatible situation, when we have only one monopoly. It's a unit that existed in a very competitive situation and was abolished. Once abolished, it was water over the dam. They are merely omitted —the operators of the unit. That is, our unit of observation is our decision unit, our group aggregate. It's everything. We have certain units in one case and other units in another. Certain units define certain ways of analysis. I don't see that there's more to it than that, but I'm willing to think about it.

KUZNETS: Suppose that what you do, every time you have a monopoly, is to nationalize it. You have the same problem if the state units and non-profit associations intervene and make economic decisions. You have the same difficulty in trying to explain them as you do, say, in trying to explain the decisions of the Communist Party by economic rationale. All I was saying is that the economic calculus can be computed only to the purely economically oriented. I'll apply methodological individualism where it can be applied, namely, where this economic calculus has a determined answer. Now, if your monopoly behaves differently because it's afraid of public pressure and so on, then it becomes a political entity. It's almost like a nationalized industry. You get the same difficulty applying economic calculus there as when you apply it to the household or to the state. The problem we're getting into is not that methodological individualism breaks down in any real sense where it's supposed to apply, but that the area to which it applies is narrowed so much because of the transformation of the size of the units, and, therefore, the dominance of the dialectical economic fact.

Q-15: I agree very much with what you have in mind. Let me give another example. You take a series of investment decisions by a multitude of simple investors. If the motivations which guide them in individual investment are truly independent of each other and of the consequences of another's action, then methodological individualism will perform well. On the other hand, if we take the allocation, over a short period, of a given stock of goods, where income distribution is given, then methodological individualism will perform well. By distinguishing types of problems where methodological individualism yields a more or less useful approximation from other important fields where it does not, the relationship between the whole and the parts might perhaps gain. I agree entirely with you that the areas where it gives a useful approximation are infinitely smaller and fewer than was thought in 1870. . . .

Q-16: . . . Infinitely fewer, but still a tremendous number of industries. I'd like to make explicit what I think was implicit in a good deal of this discussion—that one of the most important relations of the whole and the parts in economics is that we want to talk about industries as wholes, but we don't want to conceive of them as operating as wholes. We conceive of them as operating through the component parts. If the component parts saw themselves as part of the whole and interacted that way, we'd get them that way. Throughout most of classical economics, certainly in a good deal of neoclassic economics, this is very important. The distinction we constantly make is between an industry that is a collection of parts, and the individual decision units, still being the parts, that lead to a different solution than you'd come to if someone was operating the whole as a single whole. I think this is one of the most important distinctions we've made, and one that this line of questioning has emphasized, and one that individualism has taken as a primary line of assumption. There's still a lot of room for application of this logic.

Q-17: When we think of noneconomic factors, we instinctively assume that some factors, which are going to dampen or diminish the maximization urge, enter the equation, and this sometimes happens. It may distort the result that would come out of a simple maximization proposition. Very often, however, noneconomic factors enter into a noneconomical equation—and the result is to *reinforce* the maximization impulse. To put that less paradoxically, the normal real situation is that a whole set of human motives are operating; human beings are balancing impulses that lead to what looks like maximization and impulses that lead away from it. You are never dealing, with real human beings, in terms of true maximization. Sometimes noneconomic motives reinforce the maximization characteristics of the market; sometimes they push them aside.

The classical case, for example, is the Calvinist ethic or the Parsees or some minority group interested in economic operation. They 're not simply maximizing profit; they're maximizing profit plus social advantage plus anything else in which this minority group interests itself in economic operations and in profit-making operations. What I'm suggesting, then, is that if you're seriously interested in examining how markets work and introducing noneconomic factors, you can't do this simply by setting up an element of apparent economic activity and then bringing in a noneconomic element to dilute it. You've got to look at the net behavior and ask yourself whether the inevitably noneconomic factors that are operating tend to reinforce what's apparently pure market behavior or to dilute it. Sometimes, I think, you probably get what looks like supermaximization—concentrations on the pursuit of advantage beyond those that could normally be explained by the economic component in human beings. I'm suggesting, in short, that the distinction between economic and noneconomic isn't really a very useful one in the end.

KUZNETS: If it isn't useful, is there any room for the disillusioned economists?

Q-17: There's plenty of room for the disillusioned economists, but then—

KUZNETS: But how do you distinguish between economic and noneconomic?

Q-17: You've got to distinguish between motives and behavior. You can get what looks like economic behavior—maximization behavior—on noneconomic motives. There's one proposition. The other proposition is that you can have a perfectly good case for maintaining a loyalty to economics and its teachings without ever kidding yourself that this has to do directly with actual behavior in particular human situations. You may want to retain this model, along with various other models. But if you're actually studying a particular market situation, or a particular noneconomic performance, you should not assume that any noneconomic variable is or is not going to lead to economic behavior. What I'm saying is that noneconomic motives can lead to economic behavior in this sense: they can be wholly consistent and reinforce it and produce results that may go beyond the crossing of your curves.

Q-18: The last one is questionable. There is, of course, a maximization of appearance—a sham maximization that's not really a maximization. Now you put in, just as a logical gimmick, the Calvinist ethic. Then, because you put it in, you reach for a maximization. You don't really have, I think, this consequence—if only because you don't need a super, super thing. Once you have a superlative, you don't have to go above a superlative.

Q-17: You do in real life. There's no maximization in the investment process when you have uncertainty. You wouldn't build anything serious—you wouldn't invest in uncertain maximization. The risks are too big. If you're really assuming uncertainty, then this notion of an overdrive is a real thing.

Q-18: But that's a different thing. What makes the difference between a radical investment—10 per cent? 15 per cent? It's really not maximizing.

Q-17: It's the ways you approach borrower's risk and lender's risk that are very real market phenomena. This is one of the reasons I introduce the point. With respect to the investment process—expectations and risks—maximization is always the point.

Q-18: When Standard Oil decides what project it's going to invest in, goes down, and finally cuts off at 25 per cent—they say they are not interested. They are. There may be lots of reasons why they do certain very risky things that are difficult to rationalize, that the technician thinks are pretty terrible.

Q-17: No, I'm saying that it may well be that the degrees of risks taken in firms by individuals are in risk-build situations. . . .

KUZNETS: I have difficulty in distinguishing between economic behavior and economic motive. What is economic behavior?

Q-17: What are economic motives? Aren't all motives noneconomic? Isn't only behavior economic and the motives are fundamentally human or psychological or something that's extra-economic?

KUZNETS: I'm not talking about the reality now. I'm talking about the theory. I expect that the term "economic motives" seeks to apply principles of action which, under certain circumstances, will give a determinate result. I call that economic motivation although it's really only application of an assumed principle of action. It isn't motivation in the psychological sense. What is economic behavior? Economic behavior is what people do in economics—in the economic field. It may be economic behavior or noneconomic behavior in the sense of corresponding to the model or not corresponding to the model. When you are talking about the Puritan ethic, you talked in terms of what maximized economic growth.

The kind of thing the Puritans used to do with their income forced and accelerated economic growth. This was economic behavior, but in the special sense that produced economic results. In theoretical analysis, "economic behavior" corresponds to action on behalf of the decision units.

Parts and Wholes in Systems Engineering

SIMON RAMO

"PARTS AND WHOLES," the general title for this collection of lectures, is especially timely when applied to engineering. It suggests that there is a field of engineering that is concerned with the integration of the whole, as distinct from the design of its parts. This is, in fact, the field of "systems engineering."

Systems engineering—the invention, the design, and the integration of the whole ensemble—is actually an old and ever-present part of practical engineering. Any device, no matter how simple, represents to some extent a systems engineering kind of problem. This applies to a chair as well as to a transcontinental railroad, to a hand tool as well as to an intercontinental ballistic missile. There is always the need to break down the over-all problem into its component parts and to specify the requirements of each of those parts. There is always the problem of relating the parts to the whole, and the whole to the outside world that will be the user and that will expect a useful result. Why, then, is this subject particularly timely?

There is now a tremendous interest in systems engineering that did not exist a few decades ago. The systems with which we are now concerned are more complex and more difficult to engineer, and we are rapidly taking large steps in technology. Much more than in the past, a typical new system depends on immediate application of the newest discoveries of basic science. Furthermore, the relationships between the engineering considerations and the economic, military, governmental, and even sociologic considerations have become increasingly important. In these times, in which technology is altering our world so rapidly and in which government and industry must continually adjust to these changes, it is quite natural that systems engineering has become a topic of widespread interest in many circles that previously had little or no concern with it.

Right at the present, it is true, the major projects in systems engineering—that is, in the size and importance of new complexes of men and machines—are largely in the military field and related to our national survival. But it is equally true that an increasing percentage of our everyday peacetime pursuits are requiring major systems engineering. The system operations of our growing, more highly technical civilization, be they production, communications, transportation, or tax collection, are every day becoming more complex, faster paced, and geographically more widespread. In turn, this results in new interactions and interconnections among people and machines and in new over-all relationships of technology to nontechnical problems. These aspects more and more characterize modern systems engineering in its efforts to optimize the application of science and technology to create a more secure world and a more orderly one that can provide for the needs of the earth's populations.

My general plan here will be to describe the nature of systems engineering and some of the special techniques and tools required for carrying it out successfully, to comment on the teaching of systems engineering, and finally to engage in some speculations about the future.

THE NATURE OF SYSTEMS ENGINEERING

Systems engineering becomes more interesting and its problems newer and more important to us as the scope of the system grows. In discussing the general nature of systems engineering, we shall therefore most often have in mind the larger and more complex systems. Because of the breadth and complexity of our subject, we shall not find it convenient to make a complete, detailed analysis of it. Rather, we shall be able only to touch upon some of its highlights and possibilities, and to attempt in this way to convey a general feeling for the subject.

Is the New System Really Feasible?

We might start out by raising the most basic question of all: should the new system be created in the first place? For many people, the full impact of the need for going into such a question takes some time to register. The question has two broad aspects: the technical and the nontechnical.

The average systems situation is one in which the engineer is asked to meet largely technical requirements, although, of course, he is generally aware of the economic constraints on the system. Often at the start, it is known that the so-called requirements are only an ideal goal and that they cannot be met with any system that is technically feasible in the immediate future. Therefore, new and more practical requirements have to be established as the work goes along. Systems engineering in modern technology requires an unusual degree of matching the requirements and the end objectives with the state of the technical art.

Let us take, for example, an intercontinental ballistic missile. Even if the over-all objective of the systems engineer were simply to design a system that does a good job of delivering a nuclear warhead several thousand miles away—and this is too simple a description of the over-all problem—it is clear that the propulsion, guidance, structure, and re-entry problems are all wrapped up together in an exceedingly complicated relationship. If we can develop guidance systems having greater accuracy, we can achieve the necessary effect at the terminal end with less weight of warhead. Carrying a smaller warhead makes easier its protection from the tremendous heats of re-entry into the atmosphere from space. If the re-entry can be faster, if we can develop designs or materials to accept the greater heat, then there is less wind dispersion of a random type, which eases the guidance accuracy requirement. The size of the warhead (including its protection) is also related to the propulsion system because the smaller the warhead, the smaller the propulsion system that is needed to push it up to the necessary speed to travel thousands of miles. But proper control of the propulsion system is harder to achieve if high accuracy is insisted upon. It is clear that the question of technical feasibility can be difficult to answer and that a certain number of calculated risks may have to be taken along the way.

Feasibility of a major systems engineering project is not a matter of technical feasibility alone. We need to ask simultaneously whether arrangements to do the job can in fact be made. The financing of the project, the interactions with associated or displaced equipment and organizations, and the use of large quantities of technical and physical resources can all be of such consequence that the mere arrangement-making problem becomes an important parameter in the over-all systems engineering task. As an example, we know that technically we can send freight around the world by air-breathing guided missiles. But even assuming that the potential profits are attractive, can suitable financing be obtained? Will such vehicles be permitted to use existing airports or will special fields have to be built for their exclusive use? What about the hazards of collision with other aircraft? And can the new vehicles be tied in with existing systems of air traffic control? The list of such questions on a major project may be numbered in the dozens.

From all of these comments, it is evident that the practice of modern systems engineering needs to start with trying to find out what the over-all problem really is, in both its technical and nontechnical aspects, and that it could end by eliminating the problem as one that deserves no solution, or is impossible to solve within today's technical art or within our arrangement-making capabilities.

The Multiparameter Difficulty

At this point we can make the observation that modern systems engineering is characterized in part by the existence in the problem of a large number of parameters, both technical and nontechnical. Even if we limit our discussion to the technical parameters, when the number that must be considered in any problem becomes sufficiently large, it begins to be difficult to be quantitative and precise. This results in a tendency to carry out the engineering of large, complex systems in a loose manner or, at best, with purely qualitative methodology, rather than with scientific and quantitative techniques. In such instances, systems engineering becomes a matter of "opinion" or "belief," as with politics or religion. In practice, what often happens is that some of the parameters are chosen arbitrarily. Of course, the moment this is done, there is the risk that accidents and bias will control, for sometimes the parameters that have been chosen arbitrarily will turn out in the end not to be the most important.

The Systems Engineering Team

Obviously, the systems engineering team needs to include experts in all of the fields touched by the over-all system, technical and nontechnical. But since the technical part of the team is almost always much the larger part, let us examine it a bit further.

As indicated earlier, one of the frequent characteristics of modern systems engineering is that we are setting out to do things that are radical advances over the past, and in the process we have to make use of the very latest in scientific knowledge. This alone would require that the technical team include scientists who understand the newest scientific discoveries, but there is also another aspect involving scientists. In most respects, trying to understand the workings of a complex engineering system in a quantitative sense is basically not very different from the attempt by a good research scientist to understand any complex segment of nature that he is studying. We must try to write the system's laws of behavior. We must devise experiments, sometimes of a unique nature, that will test our hypotheses. The kinds of individuals capable of analyzing and predicting the actions of a complex multiparameter system are very much the same as those who seek to improve our understanding of the basic laws of nature.

But while it is true that modern systems engineering rests on a broad scientific foundation, it is also true that it is equally dependent upon known engineering techniques and upon existing components and subsystems. The practical engineer is needed not only because he has the necessary store of information on these subjects but also because he has the practical touch to make the system work as planned. This is especially important in systems containing large numbers of components with complex interconnections. Here, lack of acquaintance with the esoteric art of debugging, and with problems of reliability in what might otherwise be considered as staid old components, can prevent the success of the project so that it never gets a chance to demonstrate the progress that could have resulted from the application of new scientific discoveries.

The Human Subsystem

This discussion of the members of the systems engineering team reminds us that in the modern systems approach, most systems include men as well as machines. We cannot isolate these two parts of the system and deal with them independently and separately as though the other part did not exist. We must, in other words, think of the human beings in the system as major subsystems or components. As best we can, we must introduce their characteristics into the over-all system synthesis and analysis.

From the beginning, the human assignments must be specified, and estimated as to cost, performance, stability, and time for development. Hopefully, this is done just as clearly as we list the inanimate portions of the system and subject them to analysis. We are on weaker ground here, of course, and are less confident that we can extrapolate as we do from the relatively simpler laws of physics. On the other hand, we have had a lot of experience with human beings on which we can draw. In some situations, for example, we can unhesitatingly reject a proposed systems design because it asks too much of the human beings in the system. (By contrast, in other situations, we may find it more difficult to accept or reject a system on the basis of doubts about some simple electronic component, such as a transistor.)

We have had long experience with the extension and replacement of man's muscles by the machine. Here, it is a matter of good engineering to select those functions that can be better performed by a machine: the application of large forces, operation at high speeds, movements of precise magnitudes, operation in unfavorable environments, and the like. Ideally, we do not have a man dig a ditch; we have him steer a machine that does the digging. Man is capable of subtle motions and the application of complex combinations of forces. He should be reserved for such situations.

Something similar is indicated in the extension and replacement of man's sense and his brain. No computer or thinking machine in existence or imagined as being practical has a total capacity that is more than a tiny fraction of man's brain. It would be absurd, then, to even consider replacing man by a completely automatic system in most situations in which he uses his brain or his senses. But, again, man's remarkable system is being misused if he is given easy assignments to do—too easy for the tremendous powers of his brain and sensing system—or if the total quantity of operations is beyond the man or is tedious to an extreme. To illustrate, consider a constant decision-making operation in which there is at the most a need for deciding between two or three possibilities, easily identified, but coming at a rate of thousands per second. This is simultaneously a job too simple for the human system and yet, in sheer quantity of simple actions per unit of time, well beyond human ability to operate at all.

The degree to which a system is to be made automatic, the specialized education and training required for the human operators, and the extent to which the human eyes, ears, and brain will be used as participants in the system are all considerations that play a major part in modern systems engineering. The procedure is to some extent straightforward. We must visualize what actions need to be performed in the system; we must ask throughout whether they are best performed by a one-hundred-and-fifty-pound man or by some other total weight of automatic apparatus. We must compare the abilities, the investment, the maintenance, and the reliability of these alternates.

THE TECHNIQUES AND TOOLS OF SYSTEMS ENGINEERING

To better understand these general introductory remarks concerning the nature of systems engineering, it may help to be more specific concerning some of the techniques and the tools that are employed by the competent systems engineer. Again, we shall be able to cover only a few of the highlights of this phase of our subject.

Probability Theory

Near the top of the list of techniques and tools is probability theory. To start with, the initial specifications for a systems engineering problem must be stated in terms of probability if they are going to be truly realistic. We may wish to design a system, for example, that will shoot down enemy bombers if they come to attack us. But we have to specify what we are shooting against in terms of probabilities and not exactitudes. As a result, we have to be satisfied with describing the objectives of our proposed system in terms of a given probability of shooting down a certain fraction of enemy bombers that we have already specified as having certain probabilities of certain speeds, numbers, altitudes, and so on.

Even if we did not have to live with the probabilities of the external conditions, the performance of our system would still have to be described in terms of probabilities. For instance, every part in the system can be described only approximately. Each electronic tube, each gear, each switch, each transformer has some range within which it deviates from its optimum value (to say nothing of the occasional error that is bound to slip in). We accept this spread in faithfulness from one end of the system to the other and allow for it as best we can because to do otherwise is to ask for the impossible. To specify performance so rigidly that the spread is no longer important is to add greatly to the costs and probably delay the program at best, and for large, complex systems it would be strictly impossible.

The fact that we have in modern systems a huge number of components oftentimes of itself will require that we specify conditions of performance and of design by probable values rather than by precise ones. This is something like saying that in a Gallup Poll for a national election we must be satisfied to talk about the probable general reaction without trying to predict or measure the precise response of every individual person in the population. We do not have to have fifty million components before this concept begins to be important. We simply have to have enough, as has happened with modern systems engineering, that it becomes impractical to measure with sufficient precision the workings of each of the individual parts.

The probability problem is worth dwelling on in other respects. Most systems depend upon information transfer throughout the system, be they intercontinental ballistic missile systems, electronic banking systems, or world-wide communication systems. All components of a system capable of transmitting, handling, or storing information also have the characteristic that they produce some noise. They can never be completely quiet. Every electron tube always has electrons moving about in response to the natural interactions among the electrons and atoms caused by the local temperature of the tube. These moving electrons continuously contribute to the tube output along with any signals that are being carried. A system for information transfer must be able to outshout this natural noise, just as a home radio should be designed so that the background static is not too annoying to the ear that is trying to concentrate on the music being transmitted. This kind of noise, from the systems engineering standpoint, is only one example of the causes of errors that are produced because unwanted as well as wanted signals are being pushed through the system from one end to the other. While it is obviously desirable to have a high signal-to-noise ratio, we must also recognize that there are practical limits to how high this ratio can go. It becomes part of the systems design problem to insure that the ratio is high enough to achieve the specified probability of success in transmitting the signal without error.

As we mentioned earlier, human beings are often parts of the system. They have their own possibilities of performing their duties with errors. They, also, can introduce "noise," unwanted responses that take their place in the system on an equal basis with the proper responses.

These are some of the reasons why probability theory is one of the techniques employed extensively by the systems engineer. Actually, it would be more accurate to use the term "probability concepts" because a significant number of the problems that must be dealt with do not lend themselves well to theoretical study alone. The problems are too complicated for this to be practicable.

We shall discuss later what the systems engineer turns to under these circumstances as a tool to help him predict and understand the system.

Analysis for Unwanted Modes

The systems engineer is not only plagued by the multitude of parameters, the indefiniteness of most of them, and the need for learning to live with probability as a way of life. He also must recognize that, in addition to those characteristics that he has so carefully built into the system and that are predictable to a satisfactory degree, the system may have possibilities of operation that he does not desire. It seems to be virtually a law of nature that when a number of components (human or machine) are connected together, the modes of operation that are possible will be large in number and will include some that are undesirable. As a result, good systems engineering practice must provide for thorough, imaginative analyses and experiments to discover what the possibilities are for unwanted modes of operation and how protection against their harmful consequences may be achieved.

For example, a system designed to transmit information may include a feedback to cause the input to be influenced by the output. However, under certain conditions such a system has the ability to oscillate violently, swinging from one extreme to another, interfering not only with the transmission of the information but endangering the system itself. The resulting overloads may destroy the system by overstressing certain components if protection against this possibility is not built into the system.

The problem is much greater when one considers the human elements in the system. Presumably, if we have done a good job of matching man and machine, we have introduced the human element only when what is expected of that element is sufficiently complex, yet uniquely suited to the time delays and responses of the human body, so that it is better to employ a man than to replace him with exceedingly complicated equipment. Unfortunately, this usually means that the number of possible actions that can be taken by the human component will be very large and is almost certain to include unwanted modes.

The ultimate user himself is a common source of difficulty. To take a familiar example, in an automatic dialing telephone system it is necessary to analyze what will happen in the system if a partial number is dialed, if a nonexistent number is dialed, if the telephone is left off the hook, and if a host of other possibilities are introduced by the human element. It is not difficult to imagine how much more severe the troubles may be in more complex systems.

We can see that it is not enough to design a system so that in principle it does what it is supposed to do. It must also be designed so that it does not do what is unacceptable or unnecessary—at least, not very often.

Nonlinearity Concepts

In most modern systems we are confronted with "nonlinearity," the output does not vary directly with the input. This makes theoretical analysis difficult and complicates the testing problem. Given two alternate approaches that are otherwise equal, one linear and one nonlinear, the linear will always be favored, and properly so, because it lends itself more easily to analysis. But, as we shall see, nonlinearity can offer major advantages in some situations and is unavoidable in many others. It is therefore important that the systems engineer be well acquainted with nonlinearity concepts and the techniques for handling them.

It is common in the analysis of complex systems to try to separate the modes of operation into those that are steady-state and those that are transient, with the idea of eliminating or at least minimizing the transient modes. An example will illustrate that in some cases such an approach is short-sighted. Consider an air-to-air guided missile that leaves a mother airplane to destroy a target in its vicinity. The missile is launched with errors in direction and timing because of the imperfections of the entire system. Even if it is perfect in its direction and timing, we can only estimate what the path of the target plane will be. Hence, the missile is designed to observe the target, or to receive information from some observer, and alters its course to insure a hit or close miss (even though the commands are never perfectly stated and are changing during the course of the operation).

If the missile develops the impression through the data collection and deliberation of its guidance system that it is likely to pass to the right of the target, corrections will be introduced in its flight to cause it to travel more to the left. However, if this correction is made too rapidly, there is danger of overshoot before the missile can be redirected again toward the target. On the other hand, if we take too long to effect a correction to be sure of no overshoot, it may be too late because conditions are changing rapidly.

It may turn out, and indeed it usually does, that to obtain the optimum over-all system (including high kill rates, simple missile design, low weight, less restriction on the mother plane—to name only a few), the seeking missile should be allowed to hunt and oscillate as it closes on its target. We see, then, that in a fundamental sense the missile never does reach a steady state. It has a basic element of instability; it is oscillating, it is indecisive, it is trying to settle down but never quite achieves it before the operation is over.

Another missile, this time an intercontinental ballistic missile, further illustrates nonlinear problems. To reach a coasting speed sufficient to allow it to fall through space to its target thousands of miles away, the missile requires only a few hundred seconds of powered flight. During this period, it passes from a condition of zero speed in thick air, up to supersonic speed in thinner air, and finally into space at a speed of 10,000 miles per hour. The aerodynamic forces vary continuously, from zero at the start, to a maximum at around 35,000 feet, and back to zero as space is reached. During the same period, the missile loses weight rapidly since the largest part of the total vehicle is fuel. Not only does the mass, a strong participant in many of the operating characteristics of the missile, change drastically but the mass distribution also changes. In fact, both of these important parameters change substantially even during the short time period, a second or two, in which the large fuel tank goes through one period of the natural oscillation of a transient nature that occurs whenever the missile responds to a turning signal. Clearly, we have here a case of systems engineering in which the parameters change so rapidly during the course of the operation that nonlinear concepts are dominant in the over-all system problems.

We also have nonlinearity whenever some part of a system has limiting values or stops. Here again, in some instances, we can actually take advantage of the situation. Returning to the case of our small air-to-air missile, it makes for a simpler missile in some ways if the control surfaces are operated with small movements away from their center positions so that the turning force retains a linear relationship with the steering signal. However, it turns out upon careful analysis that by swinging the surfaces hard over to the stops part of the time, we can design a smaller, lighter missile than would otherwise be possible. So it is well worth putting up with any headaches that the nonlinearity causes.

As we have already indicated, an increasing number of systems engineering problems involve human beings as major elements. It may sound facetious to say categorically that a human being is a nonlinear element, to imply that his output does not vary proportionately to the input most of the time. Actually, depending upon the situation, a nonlinear relationship may or may not be a good approximation. In simple clerical tasks, for example, we can be reasonably confident that a nearly linear relationship exists up to the point of overload. Generally, however, we are more interested in those cases where the human being is assigned to functions that require judgments to be made of complex or unforeseen conditions. An example would be an operator's decision to shut down a plant normally under automatic control when an unforeseen condition arises, in contrast to a condition that calls for a shutdown already anticipated, which will be handled automatically without reference to the human being. Another example would be a decision that certain military intelligence information appears serious enough to call for emergency high-level analysis. Both of these examples represent a change to a different mode of operation of the system and hence are nonlinear.

In order to achieve optimum performance, it is not uncommon to find that nonlinearity in the form of multiple modes of operation should be deliberately introduced into a system. A quality control system for a high-volume operation, for example, may involve inspecting only every tenth part coming off the production line. However, as soon as an error is detected, the system immediately changes to inspecting every single part. If additional errors are detected, in excess of the statistical standards previously established, then a signal is given to shut down the line since it is probable that the manufacturing operation has deteriorated. On the other hand, if the error turns out to be random and is not repeated after a certain number of inspections, then the system will return to sampling every tenth part. Such stepwise, nonlinear variations in sampling rate are useful in a number of applications.

Many systems problems include the equivalent of a message center into which flows information pertinent to the system, be it automatic reservation-making for air lines, banking, or intelligence data-handling for the military. The problem is one of devising a rapid, economical, and simple system that will sort and disseminate the messages to the right places with the right priority. If the normal sorting system has to have a number of steps in it, with the result that there is an appreciable delay, it may prove desirable to add a quick screening process at the very beginning so that messages that appear to be urgent or important can be pulled out to bypass the normal system. Thus, again, we would have a system with different modes of operation and a switchover dependent upon the nature of the input.

Computers and Simulators

Having considered now some of the major facets of systems engineering—the many parameters, the human element, probability considerations, the many modes of operation possible, nonlinearity—we can see that the systems engineer in dealing with large, complex systems is confronted with a tremendously difficult analysis problem. Even if his sole task were to analyze and predict the performance of a system whose configuration and subsystems and components were already set, the mathematical equations necessary to describe the operation of the over-all system would be hopelessly unwieldy to solve by hand. There would be too many parts, too many nonlinear elements, too many high-order equations. Such situations can be handled only with the aid of large-scale computers and simulators.

Large digital computers have become common only during the past few years. With their high speed and large computational capacity, thousands of engineering computations can be performed in a reasonable time. This makes it practical not only to explore a wide range of values for the main parameters of the system, its subsystems, and its components, but also to study a variety of competing systems having basically different configurations. In fact, one could say that systems engineering in the truly modern sense really became possible only after the advent of the large digital computer.

Digital computers, however, can not be used conveniently or efficiently to obtain answers to all of the problems. In some cases, even they cannot solve the equations in any reasonable time, and in other cases the problems are not understood well enough for satisfactory mathematical formulation. Under these circumstances we can often turn to analog, real-time, simulation devices to predict the behavior of the system. No engineering computing center is well equipped without such devices. The ultimate in systems analysis techniques, reserved for the outstandingly difficult problems, is the connection together of computers, simulators, and an actual portion of the system, the whole becoming a simulator on a grand scale.

While in principle the concept of using simulators and computers to investigate system characteristics is straightforward, the skill required to create mathematical models and to program and set up the problems is very considerable. It is always surprising to those not experienced in modern systems engineering to learn what a large number of individuals is necessary and how high a degree of competence the individuals must possess to staff a first-rate engineering computing center. It is no exaggeration to say that there is no other phase of systems engineering that requires a higher order of talent.

The existence of computers and simulators does not mean that the process of trial and error is no longer a valuable tool in engineering. But it is no longer good engineering practice, even if it could be afforded, to construct large systems just to test them to see how they work, with the idea of then modifying them extensively. However, even though a great deal of simulation and computing is done before the system is designed, there usually still remains plenty of experimental work to be done on the actual system, and trial and error techniques are still useful.

Selecting and Optimizing the System

Generally, the systems engineer's first problem is to invent several suitable configurations to consider. These may differ substantially in their choice of subsystems and components and in their interconnections, and yet all appear to have some reasonable chance of providing the required performance. As a consequence, the systems engineer typically must analyze not just one, but several, possible approaches. Furthermore, for each basic approach he has to engage in a considerable amount of optimizing; that is, varying the parameters within the general idea of the particular configuration to seek the combination that is most advantageous.

In attempting optimization of a large system, it is not sufficient to try to optimize each subsystem or component in isolation, nor, at the other extreme, to assume that no value at all can be obtained from such isolation and that the entire system must be optimized as an integral unit. By careful study of the nature of the individual subsystems and components and their interactions, it is possible to identify those that can be separately optimized in a satisfactory fashion and those where interaction overrides and only the combination can be optimized. This task of identification is actually often more difficult than the optimization exercises themselves, but the advantages that stem from it can be worth many times the effort.

After all of the optimizing and comparing of various approaches, there may still be more than one configuration that remains in the running. There is hardly ever a single number that rates one system against another. One may be more reliable but more expensive;

another may be less desirable technically but more acceptable because it requires fewer changes in existing systems and procedures; a third, while in principle the best, will take an additional year to bring into being. The list of criteria can be both long and lacking in clarity. But one way or another, a decision must be arrived at. Hopefully, it will be prompt, and, hopefully, it will be taken with a full appreciation of the technical, as well as the nontechnical, parameters involved.

Systems Engineering Management

Having examined some of the more technical aspects of systems engineering, let us now consider the matter of management organization.

Because it extensively involves compromises among technical and nontechnical factors, systems engineering is closer to being a top management activity than is the specialized engineering that is concerned with the subsystems and the components of a system. Moreover, it is increasingly true that the large, new systems, as we advance into the more highly technological age, involve government sponsorship and government chairmanship. This brings in politics, industry-government relationships, and competition between government groups and industry groups, and between members of each of the groups. All in all, the execution of a large-scale systems engineering job requires that the systems engineer be capable not only technically, so as to be able to relate the technical parameters to one another, but also capable in a much broader sense. A good systems engineer has to be a good manager, a good "mixer," a good salesman, and a good personnel man.

Very often these nontechnical factors appear so important in the formation and execution of a new major systems engineering project that there is a tendency toward making a serious mistake in the selection of the systems engineering leadership. The top responsibility is given to a nontechnical man with the idea that this will assure the necessary attention to the nontechnical problems that a technical man might be too narrow to provide. This is often further rationalized by the argument that it will have the advantage of permitting the technical man to concentrate on the strictly technical pursuits. What actually happens, instead, is that large amounts of technical effort are wasted because of inadequate management.

It is true, of course, that the top systems engineering manager should possess a broad appreciation of the nontechnical as well as the technical problems. But the technical capability is a necessary ingredient. Without it the systems engineering quickly becomes loose, qualitative, and intuitive, and the system is designed and brought into being without very much of an effort that deserves to be called systems engineering. It ought to be obvious, even though apparently it is not, that the manager of a complex systems engineering project should be outstanding technically.

THE TEACHING OF SYSTEMS ENGINEERING

With an indication of both the difficulty and the breadth of the over-all systems engineering function, it is appropriate now to discuss the teaching of systems engineering. Formal teaching of the subject is of course only one approach to the problem of creating good systems engineers. Another approach, and the one that has been almost the sole method in the past, is to allow systems engineers to come out of the specialized branches of engineering as they mature and as their capabilities become manifest for the broader task of interactions among the various technical fields. The apprenticeship idea is somewhat similar. The younger men who give indications of promise for this kind of work are assigned to systems engineering teams where they work with experienced systems engineers to learn the ropes.

One plan for teaching systems engineering would be to select a broad group of basic courses, rather than attempting some sort of systems engineering course per se that, like courses in electrical engineering and aeronautical engineering, would have the objective of producing a person trained to work in the particular field. Such a plan would certainly stress breadth of scientific knowledge but perhaps would also include some specialization in one field of engineering. Learning to reduce scientific concepts to practice in engineering applications is a necessary part of the systems engineer's background, and he can probably learn this more easily by some concentration in a specialized field. The basic course, however, would feature such subjects as stability theory, nonlinearity, random phenomena, information and communication theory, the principles of energy conversion, the theory of computers and simulators and their programming and utilization, and other disciplines that are especially needed by the systems engineer.

To follow this, we could arrange graduate courses based upon case studies. Ultimately, case studies can be expected to disclose major generalizations; some of these are available today. These generalizations—the principles of systems engineering—could then be illustrated by examples that would be fragments of over-all systems engineering design problems. We could, for example, point out that in general the interconnection of a large number of components creates other modes in addition to the one that is intended. The student could then be given as homework a series of examples in which he would be asked to look for such other modes and to show how some could be disastrous if not taken into account in the design. Similarly, the student could be taught the principle that errors accumulate in a system from indefiniteness in specification and indefiniteness in performance and that this goes on from one end of the system to the other. Then problems would be assigned showing that the errors do not necessarily add linearly, but in a more complex way, sometimes giving surprising relationships between the output and the input. And that what superficially appears to be a satisfactory system is one so replete with errors that it is likely to contribute only confusion rather than to perform a useful mission.

I believe that the selection of students is much more of a problem in systems engineering than it is in the specialized branches of engineering or in the general study of science. Some people are competent, or even brilliant, only when they are allowed to deal with a narrow topic in great depth. Only a few can be comfortable and productive when they deal constantly with interactions of many fields and can afford, on any individual system, to look only at the grosser characteristics of the components that make up the system. The situation is aggravated further by the fact that the top levels of systems engineering should be staffed only by individuals who can mix technical and nontechnical matters. We clearly can provide courses that will aid any intelligent student in understanding the nature of systems engineering and in increasing his chances of helping a systems engineering team. But if he trains for physical science in general or for a specialized field of engineering, it is somewhat easier for him to branch out later toward systems engineering, if he is properly suited to it, than it is for a person trained specifically in systems engineering to switch to a more specialized field if he finds that he is more likely to be successful in a narrower field.

When it comes to training a person for top responsibility in systems engineering, I think the problem is one step worse than training students to be executives. There are many courses that can be of aid, particularly if there has been a proper selection of students, but in some ways attempting to train a man for a "high" job in school is a little like training a man for leadership by giving him courses entitled "Advanced Courage" or "Principles of Heroism."

THE FUTURE OF SYSTEMS ENGINEERING

Let us turn now to the future of systems engineering. The art and the science of systems engineering are still in their infancy. We can expect that they will undergo great changes in the future, particularly since we have not reached anywhere near the limit in the complexity and scope of systems of men and machines. But such more advanced systems will assuredly be created to provide for the operations of our increasingly technical society, whether it is at peace or at war. Thus, our discussion must be based upon speculation about the nature of these future systems.

This speculation can perhaps best be accomplished by means of an example. The broad example that we shall choose here is one that I believe will become the greatest growth industry of the next decade or two. It encompasses those systems in which the machines are engaged to a significant degree in intellectual pursuits, relieving man of routine mental effort.

Such systems have both military and peacetime applications: in manufacturing, banking, ballistic missile defense, education, and even in the practice of law and medicine. All of these applications have certain fundamentals in common. There is a wide need for systems to receive and process information, to change its form, to store new information along with the old, to arrive at logical conclusions, to decide on actions, and to observe the results—all the while maintaining high accuracy as well as handling large quantities of data. Of course, we already have the beginnings of such systems. But they probably are not very much further along than was the development and utilization of mechanical power a few years after the invention of the steam engine.

Parenthetically, it would be convenient to have an appropriate word to refer to the kind of systems we are discussing, and I would like to suggest "intellectronics," derived from "intellect" and "electronics."[1]

Intellectronics systems appear destined to become in the near future the number one area of military priority. We now have a world situation in which one nation can inflict thermonuclear destruction on another within a few minutes after making the decision, even though the distance between the nations is thousands of miles. We have already passed the point where the highest priority is given to the weapon of destruction, the bomb, and we are about to pass the point where the highest priority goes to the method of delivering it. Very soon, the problem of command and control will move into first place. The military will require means for observing, analyzing, communicating with, and integrating activities covering the entire earth. A tremendous quantity of complex information, much of which will be changing rapidly, will have to be surveyed and processed into sound conclusions and decisions in a

[1] Such words as "computer," "automation," "cybernetics," "data handling," and others have been used to describe various limited aspects of the over-all field in which basically the human intellect is extended by a technology that is customarily described by the word "electronics." But there has been no word that is suitable for the general identification of the over-all field.

matter of minutes. This will require systems of intelligent human beings and extensions of their intellectual capability through electronics.

Similarly, in most of our peacetime intellectual pursuits, the problems are becoming ever greater. The number of factors to be considered; the speed required; the amount of information to be absorbed, pondered, and acted upon; and the increasing need for recognizing the detailed interactions between parts of our total operations—all of this, too, is bringing into first place the need for systems that extend the intellectual capacity of the human being.

To review briefly what has been said earlier, the best possible match should exist between man and machine. Human beings have intellectual capacities well beyond the largest electronic machine imagined to be practical. On the other hand, our brain power is not suitable for some purposes because our brains have been shaped by the forces of evolution to make them especially useful for other functions. For example, the human brain put to the job of adding short columns of one-digit numbers is able to perform at the rate of about two numbers per second. Even this low rate is accompanied by considerable error and early fatigue, but machines can do such processing at rates of from thousands to millions per second. Here, as in the industrial revolution in which man's muscles as simply power-producing means were replaced by the machine, man's capability is qualitatively superior but quantitatively inferior. High-quantity, high-rate jobs should be assigned to the machine, elevating man to the higher intellectual tasks for which he is uniquely suited.

With machines and human brains more and more acting as partners in intellectual pursuits, we can expect considerable influence on natural language and, more generally, on the form in which information is recorded and transmitted. We know that in principle we can provide electronic machines to translate a collection of words, phrases, or sentences in one natural language to a different language, retaining the same (or nearly the same) thought. Automatic translation can meet an important need and will undoubtedly become common. But as an improved balance is achieved between the roles assigned to the human brain and to the machine, it becomes foolish to limit information to those forms whose only recommendation is that they have been inherited from the customs of long-past centuries. Instead, we can expect that the engineering of intellectronics systems will include the specification of a new language—one that is more precise and that is specifically suitable for a man-machine system. And since the basic principles of such systems will be essentially the same all over the world, possibly we can see here the first faint glimmerings of forces that are sufficiently fundamental to bring about the adoption of a universal language, if only to cover a portion of man's communications needs.

As an increasing number of military, governmental, business and professional activities call upon the inventive genius of the systems engineer for solutions to a wide variety of their problems, systems engineering will become more and more concerned with the larger national issues. Included among these issues will be those that will determine the success of our transition to the coming highly technical age. It is thus not inappropriate as a final summary of all that has been said about the nature of systems engineering and its trend in the future, to consider how it might be applied to the matter of education.

In the educational systems of our nation today, the educational process is an intellectual task performed largely by human beings who are trained in the processes of teaching and in the subjects that they teach. The teachers on occasion are provided with minor machine aids such as slide projectors, movies, and television. In the educational system of the future, however, by applying the principles of systems engineering to the entire process, we can expect to come up with a substantially different configuration, one that will take maximum advantage of the unique capabilities of the human intellect by providing it with much more extensive help from machines. Obviously, we cannot presume here to invent an optimum system—the problem is much too complex for a quick, off-the-top-of-the-head solution. But, if the reader is generous, we can engage in some speculation that is at least illustrative of the nature of systems engineering, even though we may not actually succeed in making a significant contribution to the design of the educational process of the future.

The systems engineering approach would commence with an attempt to be specific about the goals of the educational process. If we want to teach the child to reason, if we want him to know certain facts, if we want him to be able to use certain intellectual tools, we should list these as specifically as possible. We likewise will need to specify means for judging how well the system is meeting these goals. In addition, we shall want to take measurements before, during, and after the educational process to aid us in determining how the system may be improved. We can expect to find that the system of education we design will involve a man-machine partnership. It may not look very much like the school of today, which makes only incidental use of recent advances in technology.

Any good educational system basically must provide for imparting information, helping the student to understand it if new and difficult concepts are involved, and reinforcing and testing his memory and understanding by questions and problems. The system we are going to invent will be no exception. To illustrate what might come from a modern systems engineering approach, we shall take an individual course as an example. Since we have not actually made a systems analysis, we shall be imagining freely and shall ask the reader to be liberal in his judgment of the design.

Let us say that our course is in the principles of trigonometry. In our new system, the trigonometry student might spend an hour or two a week in the company of other students in what looks something like a classroom of today, observing a film which places trigonometric principles before him. The film employs both a human lecturer and animation. This classroom, however, is not an ordinary one. Each seat includes a small console, which is wired up to the central data processor of the school. (Incidentally, the machine records who is in attendance at the class. When the student sits down, he identifies himself to a little input device at each seat by the name tag that he carries or by his thumbprint, depending upon whether it is the year 1980 or the year 2000.) Continually during the "lecture," questions are put to the class by the film, and the students push buttons to give their answers to the central data processor. Two things happen during the lecture as a result of the interconnections between the student consoles, the film, and the central data processor. First, a record is kept of the progress of each of the students. Second, the film automatically may be lengthened with additional information added, or shortened with some redundancy removed, in accordance with instructions from the central data processor, which knows what fraction of the class appears to be understanding the material.

But this lecture hall session is only the beginning of the process of teaching trigonometry. There are at least two more steps. In the second step the student finds himself spending an hour or two a week in private with a machine that is much more complex than the lecture hall console. When he identifies himself to this machine, the central data processor automatically refers to its detailed record of his individual progress. It also has some built-in instructions that are the product of a careful analytical study of the results of alternate approaches to the teaching of trigonometry. These have been prepared by educational specialists, both in the teaching process per se and in the subject of trigonometry. As a result, the central data processor is able to make an automatic choice as to what additional material this particular student should have, and what additional examinations should test his comprehension. In response to signals from the central data processor, the individual machine then commences to present from its store of material a selection especially tailored to the progress of that particular student. Moreover, and this is essential, the machine continues to be engaged in a responsive (one could almost say sympathetic) relationship with the student so that his questions determine not only the pace but the selection of material presented. If the student shows, for example, that he still fails to understand a particular concept after it has been presented twice, the machine then automatically shifts to an entirely different way of presenting the material, which has been found in some instances to be more easily understood by certain students.

At this point we can see that machines, in the form of intellectronics systems, can be used to create a teacher-student relationship, and that a number of the functions now thought of as exclusively within the province of the human teacher can in principle be transferred to machines. Machines are not limited to the mere presentation of material and the handling of examinations. Machines actually can carefully select and adjust their operations to the apparent needs of the individual student just as a teacher would do if he were able to concentrate on only one student.

In our new system, it is only in the third step that a direct relationship exists between the student and a human teacher. Here, as with the physician aided by his X rays and electrocardiograms, the highly trained teacher (diagnostician would really be a better word) regularly examines the detailed record of the progress of the individual student. The student's responses to questions, his speed of learning, the results of his examinations and of his aptitude tests are all readily available from the central data processor. The teacher discusses with the student any significant difficulties that the record indicates exist, or any problems that the student feels he has. Depending upon the circumstances, the teacher may then introduce into the intellectronics system some special changes to help the student to get as much as possible out of the course in trigonometry.

Finally, such special changes, and indeed every bit of data associated with the system, are subjected to extensive analysis, done in part by machines and in part by human beings, with the objectives of finding improved techniques of teaching, improved settings for the system, and improved techniques of diagnosis.

Even though the details of our imagined system may prove in time to be grossly inaccurate, it does seem fairly certain that a systems engineering approach to the matter of education would produce some kind of a complex system of men and machines. This could result in what in effect would be several new professions and at least one new industry. The creation of such systems would probably be undertaken by a specialized industry that would employ not only experts in electronics and systems engineering but also experts in the subjects to be taught and in the principles of education. In turn, a typical school faculty would include individuals trained to handle the broad application of the new system to the educational process, and numerous specialists in the analysis of student progress, the goals, the examinations, and the interview techniques. A number of the faculty members also would act as consultants to industry in the creation of new programs and new systems.

We do not expect, of course, to substitute a system-engineered educational system for our present one all of a sudden. For one thing, we will require experimentation for years with the various major subsystems and with simulated setups in order to work out critical aspects of the new system. For another, any step toward substantial extension of the teaching process through electronics must gradually be absorbed into and somehow be paralleled with the existing system.

As with all modern systems engineering approaches in general and with intellectronics systems in particular, the educational system of the future will be distinguished by the way in which the human being is reserved for those tasks to which he is uniquely suited. The erroneous impression should not be allowed to exist that the systems engineer has only or even largely the task of designing machines to replace the human being. The teacher will clearly not be replaced by machines any more than the doctor is replaced by X-ray machines or electrocardiographs. Instead, the human beings engaged in the teaching process will be doing that which is suited to their remarkable intellectual capacities, and they will be relieved of those tasks that can be better assigned to machines that extend human intelligence. The partnership of the human intellect with the machine makes a stronger, more sensible teaching team.

In this last example, then, we have seen or can easily imagine all of the characteristics of systems engineering problems at play: the multiple parameters, the interactions among parts of the system, the variety of disciplines involved, the matching of man and machine, nonlinearity, the difficulty of predicting performance for a complex system, the problem of unwanted modes, the problem of optimizing the system, the need for statistical rather than precisely quantitative descriptions, the uncertainties introduced by the human element, and finally the difficulties associated with the nontechnical problems of economics, politics, and existing organizations.

DISCUSSION

Parts and Wholes in Systems Engineering

Q: I am wondering if you would discuss what you feel will be the biggest revolution in the application of systems engineering in the next decade—and some of its problems.

RAMO: I think this is really an elaboration of the point I made in my talk. Today, we have a fad on space. Recently, we had one on nuclear physics. Before that it was electronics, introduced as a new term to the public and illustrated by pictures of electrons chasing around a nucleus. In the case of nuclear physics, there was no need to change the figure at all. Now space has come in and we haven't had to change the diagram either.

I think the future has to do with extending human brain power. The fast tastes of the world—the interactions, the large volume of considerations that have to be brought to bear, the trillions of messages that have to be brought from one part of the earth to another in order to keep the physical operations of the earth going—suggest that something very new has to be added. And this is the extending of man's brains. It's simply the comeback of electronics with more specificity for the future. The extending of human brain power will come closer to determining the future positions of nations than some things that are more popular with the press today. If Soviet Russia goes faster, then some time we'll be aware of their control of the spectrum. There'll be a fight to get your signal through, to control the physical processes of the earth by having the greater control over the transmitting and handling of information. Accordingly, the most interesting problems of the future will be those where, basically, a collection of men and machines doing an intellectual task will be invaded by these methods.

Q: Would you care to comment on the problem as we everyday human beings will find ourselves involved with it?

RAMO: Well, there are two classes of problems. One is purely economic—a twenty-five dollar human brain extension rather than a twenty-five million dollar one. Military sponsorship today is too nearly the total source of support. The steps needed are big and speculative. The economic problem sets a limitation on the engineering problem in a narrow sense—until we find not only ways of making the components cheaper, but perhaps ways of forming complete networks of components very cheaply.

The next point is not yet realized as much as may finally be the case—the human component. There's been too much use of the word computer. You buy a computer to do all of these jobs. You tackle intellectual pursuits with a combination of men and machines. We don't understand the men well enough. We need to do a lot of systems engineering on what the whole operation is supposed to be, when men are involved. But you can't barge into these systems. You go into a banking system and say "Now we'll help out here. Awful lot of stuff to keep track of and it costs them a lot. Surely, there's a better way of doing it. Human beings are being used improperly. They're using a trivial fraction of their total capacity." But too often people want to come in and replace the teller. They keep the system designed around humans and not designed around the concept of machines. It's something like designing an earth moving machine that looks a lot like a shovel—not the same size, but with the same mechanism. But that doesn't pay. You might as well hire the labor. It'll cost you about the same per hour to employ either one of them. You have to think in terms of a different approach—and a match of man and machine—to do the job. In that sense, systems engineering and human engineering are bottlenecks. Those things taken together—just understanding what it is we're working with—determine what the goals are.

Q: In respect to the new education system as a machine system, how do you make this system fail-safe?

Ramo: I'm not sure it has to be fail-safe. You want a good educational system. Now, it should not create too many tragedies, such as ruining a certain number of kids. Whatever you do, you shouldn't confuse tentative designs with not having a tentative design. One tentative design is things just as they are. Someone has already designed a system for me—a bad one—and now he's attacking it. You must compare these systems. It may turn out that doing it precisely as we do it today is the best system, possibly with the addition of a little television. But you should start out asking, what is it we're trying to do? what are the intellectual processes involved? on what level of intellectual capacity can the machine do better? Then try to match the things up. You can't have something that fails all the time, or fails more frequently than the present system, without seriously considering rejecting that system. But fail-safe doesn't happen in nature to 100 per cent.

Q: I believe you spoke of the design of government as a problem for systems engineering? What are your thoughts on that?

RAMO: I don't remember doing that.

Q: I thought you mentioned government and politics.

RAMO: What I meant to indicate at that point—mind you, I'm not rejecting the question—was that government and the way it works—its requirements—is a factor in large systems engineering projects a good deal of the time. This is something you must list as a characteristic of large-scale systems engineering projects. When it comes to design of government, I would say this is one step more difficult, on the average, even than education. I want to use an even more ambitious example—some of the features of systems engineering in the large sense. I would say you set down national goals, parameters of the world. Certainly you could take a segment of government that is concerned with a limited task and ask what it is that they're trying to do with a group of human beings. You'll find they're engaged in information-processing for decision-making. In general, you can look at the entire operation and separate it into pieces that you understand very well. Some of the pieces of work machines can do better. Certainly this applies to the military. They are doing just this.

Q: I'd like you to amplify your point about fail-safe. If we do succeed in developing these new electronics systems, how do we assure ourselves that we are not creating a 1984?

RAMO: You mean rather than 1970? What is it that you mean by 1984?

Q: A world of close control of everything an individual does, with a card in an IBM machine or a segment of a piece of tape.

RAMO: I think I understand what you mean and I've thought about it. The problem is beyond me, but I'll give you a few speculative comments about it. We are concerned with the possibility that we may be moving toward a type of world that we don't like. The physical operations, and the control thereof, keep the world going and catch all of us in them. But freedom of choice in the usual sense is more and more denied to us. If you're worried about that, then more than ever, you need to believe that whatever we do in the physical operation should be subjected to a systems engineering approach.

Surely, we need to have things made for us to use, food grown, people and things moved about, and the whole physical operation controlled. But it does not follow that certain other things that we associate with freedom and the good life need to fall by the wayside. But it could happen, if it is done incorrectly. This suggests a type of national planning—executive and Congressional departments, I suppose—in which you look at the world of the future and you set down those things that are fixed parameters. These result from the fact that we do have airplanes in the skies, do have food to produce. There are other things, however, that are not fixed and in which we have choices. I think we need to see both those characteristics of the world ahead so that we can design a system of operation to give us the maximum of clarity.

In other words, if in 1984 we're both alive and sitting around speculating on a lot of interesting subjects, not a bit concerned that we put in a certain number of hours a day in a certain profession, having ample choice left to us, is that the best way to do it? Out of many things for which we are suited—we have been educated and the educational process has involved a lot of sensible examination of what our capabilities are, a better bringing out of our capabilities—we sit and speculate about how to do this educational system over, and wonder whether we've done the right thing, and we enjoy this.

Then we sit down and draw beautiful pictures of what the backside of Venus looks like—something we're privileged to do because there are trips to Venus and we have taken them. We have a choice of whether to go there or someplace else. All that's necessary is to walk up to the machine, identify where and when you want to go, and it will either say "O.K.," or suggest alternate dates and places. If too many people are calling for a trip to Venus and getting a busy signal, the system will automatically generate more rockets to Venus, and the whole thing will be rectified to give the maximum freedom of choice.

You should still be able to walk in and pick your necktie. But when you pick that necktie out, you don't use the old system of paying money to a young lady who, having finished high school and taken some interesting subjects, now stands behind a counter, filling out little pieces of paper, giving you one and putting one down, so that another girl like her can take them and add them to other pieces of paper. The frequent outcome of this procedure is that instead of waiting on you, she's busy reading a magazine and wishing you hadn't come in; and you can't blame her. Instead of that, you pay her for your necktie by putting your thumb print on the store's account. Speaking of fail-safe, if occasionally a transistor should go wrong, then the city or your whole account may be wiped out. This would be what you'd have to expect of life in that period.

Q: I think that that is a very good example. I'm not sure that this is really such a poor man-machine relationship. Isn't it true that most of the people, most of the time do the things they do for reasons that are hardly connected with any internal system or primary aim? I'm reminded of a cartoon showing a dictaphone salesman talking vigorously at a typical executive with a dictaphone sitting on his knee, looking quizzically at it. It didn't feel quite right. At what level of a system does the fact that people do what they're doing for unrelated reasons simply have to be considered?

Ramo: In a narrower problem, certainly it would be true that you would assume the impact of social relationships, in general, on everything that you do involving a human being. But I feel confident of one thing: We are so far away from the proper match of human beings and their intellects to the pursuits of life that you can't for years and years invade the most extreme mismatches and rectify them without major losses that aren't anywhere near the gains. Surely, almost all of us during the day do some things that don't match with our brains. I know that driving in Los Angeles certainly doesn't match with my brain. I do it not by my brain but that part of me that is a substitute for courage. If I apply my brain to the problem, it discourages me from taking to the highway. In the old days, when I used to travel on trains, I used to worry about those fellows who came along and hit the axle to make a test, then went along to hit the next one, oftentimes with a light in the winter darkness. I used to suffer for them. There must be some medical name for it—the problem of imagining that I was in the other guy's shoes. I can imagine this so well that I actually suffer from the boredom and the discouragement of doing a thing that is so unsuitable for human beings. And surely it is so similar to what most jobs offer.

Now, it's not so much the cost of the system that runs into millions of dollars per year; it's the poor use of the human beings. What they're doing just isn't interesting enough. After a few days, clerks get over the initial satisfaction of looking into all these accounts to see what they're like—how big and how many. It isn't fun any more. We've gotten so mismatched that we grasp at any diversion, like one of Pharaoh's slaves transporting those big stones. Occasionally, there's a twig sticking out; he reaches down and pulls it out; and he's really gotten his satisfaction of the day. He's been able to do something other than just exert his tiny little fraction of horsepower. Somehow, the Pharaoh, who gets a big kick out of watching this thing and looks at one of these slaves as merely a machine, would get nothing like the same kick if a bulldozer were doing the job. How is he going to get his kicks? He just has to get them some other way.

(*A series of diverse questions is asked.*)

RAMO: The first thing that comes to my mind is the breadth of these questions. I wonder whether I should pose as a spaceman or an intellectronics man, because the technical man in the fad area is able to answer any and all questions. I'm not worried about that, because crises will continue to occur long after I've gone. But for the future, it seems to me human beings still will be capable of controlling the system. Once the system fails to satisfy them, they'll probably start to destroy it, and each other, and get down to a smaller population with the old ways.

Maybe in the end—and this is the real use of space—if you don't like things here, you can arrange to go there because enough people want it and the machines are producing huge rockets. Nothing keeps us from building a huge thing to transport a group of men and women and ministers, with means of interchanging matter and energy that will be developed at that point, so as to have a whole cycle, and choose orbits and have things your own way. So in the intellectronics period, where man and machine are matched intellectually to take care of the physical operations of the world and keep from having chaos, there will be time to think about these problems. Maybe the thing to think about is that it's going to be a lot more fun than we anticipate.

Q: In the intellectronics age, would you expect that a great deal of work would have to be done on motivation research, bringing together more of our knowledge of the cognitive aspects of human behavior with the motivations? What makes people happy? What do people want to do?—

RAMO: I'm afraid I will lose some of the aspects of this question if you go on to the next one. There's only one comment I feel capable of making in response to that first question. I think the kind of systems that we're tending toward will have a means for doing it better and faster than we do today. I almost inadvertently touched on the answer in another question—the aspect of people being able to choose where they wanted to go for their vacations. You'll get some quick answers to at least some aspects of motivation. This is part of what I meant earlier when I said that the intellectronics world doesn't have to be regimented, and may in fact be far superior, in terms of getting what people want or should want by finding out what it is that they do want. Basically, this is information processing on a grand scale, while the physical operations providing the wherewithal go on, with a minimum of intervention, to serve the needs.

Q: The way you talk about a class of candidate solutions offers a way for the social scientist to get at the problem of rationality. You are working toward a distinction in human behavior, in which candidate solutions for a course of action are examined not only as to the rewards that they will bring if applied, but also as to the cost of finding them. The cost of searching, of thinking, of changing is a major factor in the behavior of decision units. In other words, you get the systems and search for the strategic links. You have a world of people who think in an old-fashioned way, using essentially whatever biological equipment they have under their thatch. And, on the other hand, you have a very few places that are far in advance of these others. Would you comment on the links between the two?

As an example, today we spend a vast amount of money on the storage of books and very little on indexing. What we index we do not put on punched cards in any way a machine can get at the information. Handbooks are not available in forms appropriate for machine processing. It would cost several thousand dollars just to get this stuff in order. Most of the experts in subject areas have no statisticians available to them with whom they could work. Could anything be done to work on this crucial area? Again, for the teaching system—most textbooks are nowhere near the shape necessary to feed them into the trial machine. Can you do something with this?

RAMO: I'm so glad you asked this question. When I referred to extending human brain power as the big thing in the position of nations, I was thinking that everything we do—whether it be the physical operations, education, law research—it all gets back to information. It is all dissemination, processing. We find that our present pattern, built up over the years, is unsuited to the age that we see shaping up. I mentioned language translation. That's a small part, but it brings up a big thing. It's one thing to talk about translating from Russian to English, but how about from English into English? How about the problem of taking the essential plots out of our literature and making them readily available—thinking in terms of the clues and essential items in order to get at the background of the things you want. Some of this can be described by the words "indexing," "sorting," and "correlating." But it is also information retrieval. Taking all this together, I feel confident that there will be radical changes. As they begin to come forward, they will influence first, written language—the storage of information, the way in which it is put forth—and from that, oral language.

It may be that the machine condition to the intellectual process has to begin with information. It may be the real power to affect the changes in language that have been theoretical for centuries, for the machine can follow information coming from all parts of the country and all parts of the world, in different industries and organizations that have their local formats for handling information. The machine is objective. It says: "I don't care who you are, where you came from, or how you've been doing. If you want me to do the job well, quickly, easily, make it all economical, and communicate with other machines, I want the information in this form. Out of this will come the type of life that you want."

Now this brings up the question that some will ask right away: What happens to Shakespeare and the beauty of language? It doesn't follow that whatever it is that we would miss has to be missed in principle; the mode of transmission has to be changed. One would still be able to express the most subtle of thoughts, but would become accustomed to express them in a different manner. It also could be that a great fad would sweep the earth. The attorney, when he wants to look at the past, would be able to be in contact with a few million past positions, just for a particular problem. Since people have leisure now, one of the things they do is sit around and read old things—not just Shakespeare, but books, rhymes, *New Yorker* articles. We enjoy them; it's something like collecting antiques, part of the background of the human race. We sit around and talk about whether we have or haven't lost something. If the information is going through at a great rate, then we're more efficient on doing the things to assure what we want from the physical operations.

Q: Could we say that the conception of parts-whole which is entertained really governs the kind of programming of the machines and also would be necessary for the carrying out of the future development you're speaking of? Until we do get a conception of parts-whole, are we going to be able to do this?

RAMO: I think we have a bit of a chicken and egg problem. The Egyptians building the Sphinx is one example. Suppose we walked up to the Pharaoh and said: "Look, this is no way to do things. It's wrong to use people in this manner. It's beneath human dignity. They're quantitatively unsuited; they're qualitatively above it." He then asks: "How do I build this space?" You say, "Tractors, bulldozers" and start figuring out what's needed. We have to drill oil wells to get the gasoline. It's quite a project. The Pharaoh looks at it and says it's economically unsound; it would take too long; and, even if you're right, you're way ahead of your time.

Now, somehow, the year 2010 is one we can imagine. Certain things seem to be fixed; the rest, presumably, is open to choice. Now the problem is how to get there from here, and to design what we want from choice. Surely, it isn't going to happen this way. We are not smart enough to do it well. Take airline navigation and traffic control—surely we will have chaos before we have a world-wide traffic-control system. With the increase of numbers and points that enter the system—amount of traffic, people, and freight; the increased spectrum of speeds from the zero speed of the helicopter up to the space ballistic delivering in half an hour at the other side of the world; operations in all weather with increasing demand—we have to create a system which makes traffic control semi-automatic by balancing people and machines. To put this together in the United States alone, we'd have to get together the Army, the Navy, and the Air Force, the CAA, the CAB, the State Department, the Commerce Department, the airlines, the companies that make airplanes, computers, and communications. By the time you put all of this together and get the arrangements made through systems engineering, it will be needed a lot more than it's needed today—and it is needed today. The way we seem to arrive at change is by things getting so bad that some desperate thing is done. Yet, somehow, it'll get there, even by false starts and confusion, because this is the direction in which it's got to go.

Parts and Wholes in Cultural Analysis

CLYDE KLUCKHOHN

ANTHROPOLOGISTS deal with cultural phenomena at two levels that overlap but that it is important to distinguish conceptually. The first level is primarily explanatory or comparative, while the second is descriptive and particularistic. The contrast is between culture in general and specific cultures looked upon as unique assemblages. One may conveniently speak of "general-culture" and of "unique-culture." In the first case, attention is focused upon the fact of similarities of a particular kind in human life all over the world. The widest generalization is that between human nature as biologically constituted and responses to the environing situation there is always interposed the intervening variable of culture. Except for a few simple reflexes and under conditions of extreme physiological stress, members of the species *Homo sapiens* do not respond directly to a stimulus or a stimulus field. Their behavior is influenced by conventional definitions or interpretations of stimuli. Though limited by the facts of biology and psychology, such systems of conventions can never be derived from such facts. They are the products of the historical process. "Culture" in this sense is a category of a generality comparable to "gravity" or to "disease," and it is essential to the understanding of almost all human behavior. There are also, however, more specific similarities encompassed under general-culture. There is the so-called universal cultural pattern. This phrase reflects the circumstance that some patterns turn up in all culture. For example, marriage always appears; murder is always differentiated from justifiable homicide; every culture includes prohibition of some of the varieties of incest. Then there are the similarities that are not universal or nearly universal but rather associated with specific types of cultures. For instance, agricultural societies that construct elaborate buildings ordinarily manifest likewise the characteristics of social classes and a priest-temple-idol cult.

On the other hand, when the anthropologist is concerned with unique-culture, his attention is placed upon the ultimate and irreducible distinctiveness of each specific life-way. From the level of abstractness represented by "agriculture," "social class," and "cult" the anthropologist proceeds to details of content and styling. What particular crops are grown and how? Is membership in a class ascribed or acquired? How are priests selected and trained? The more abstract cultural phenomena that are universal or that have a wide distribution in space and time are presumably more basic or constant, more directly referable to common and inescapable factors of human biology and of generalities in the human condition. Features that lend uniqueness are the secondary and variable ones, more immediately traceable to the accidents of history. They are nevertheless of great scientific interest, and here I shall consider only unique-culture.

The study of unique-culture (henceforth I shall omit the qualifier, "unique") departs from the demonstration of certain regularities or recurrences in human behavior that, in their totality, distinguish one human group throughout a specified period of time from all other human populations. I say "certain" regularities because there are recurrences in human behavior that are not cultural. All peoples eat and sleep. One does not arrive at the cultural realm until one has information as to how and when a particular people eats and sleeps and what they report about their eating and sleeping. In short, the student of culture is interested in those repetitive behaviors that involve a selection from two or more alternatives that are physically possible and functionally effective, that—from the standpoint of a detached observer—are equally open. Hence, to say that a people who live near a body of water fish is not, strictly speaking, a cultural statement. On the other hand, the report that a group who have easy access to nutritious fish make no attempt to catch them or refuse to eat certain varieties of fish is definitely a cultural statement. So, likewise, a detailed description of the technology of fishing, from whom and in what manner the techniques of fishing are learned, and the standard rationales for fishing in one way rather than another.

The qualifying phrase "in their totality" is equivocal. There would be general agreement among anthropologists that one cannot properly speak of two distinct cultures unless there is a significant discontinuity between two total life-ways. Again, abstractly, there is consensus that "small variations" by geographical region or social class or occupation give rise to various subcultures of a single, over-all culture. But what constitute "small variations"? Most anthropologists, if pressed, would probably reply that they intend something analogous to the criteria applied to differentiating dialects from languages. These operations boil down to the following: if members of two speech communities can understand each other, albeit with some difficulty, then they are speaking dialects of the same language; if they can at most (as with English and German) recognize occasional cognates, then we have two languages. I think that the parallel is along the right lines. When a naive participant in one group enters another group and feels reasonably comfortable, reasonably at home, when he knows about what will happen next in familiar types of situations, it is probable that he has merely moved in cultural dialect: from one subculture to another. Obviously, however, this is far too rough and ready. Anthropologists are not yet able to say—or at any rate to agree—as to how "significant" discontinuities may be defined. Language will often but not always serve as a major test. There is such a thing as "Swiss culture" in spite of four languages. Conversely, Mexican culture is not to be equated with Spanish, although the national language is the same in both cases. Nor will nationality do. One can think of instances where culture flows beyond political borders, and there are multicultural states such as Yugoslavia. At certain extremes one can point to acceptable discriminators. A group whose economic base was hunting and gathering could never be regarded as having a culture that was a subculture of an industrial culture. I do not think any anthropologist would be happy with positing two related subcultures in one of which residence was matrilocal and in the other patrilocal. What these and similar illustrations suggest to me is that anthropologists are convinced that some features of a culture are more diagnostic or determinative of the totality than others. So much so indeed that in some instances a single fundamental difference is taken as sufficient to establish a "significant discontinuity."

In this context what does "significant" imply in anthropological thought? There are two implications of basic relevance to our subject:

(1) no culture can be isolated or characterized by even the most exhaustively correct enumeration of its parts;

(2) there is some notion of hierarchy among the components of a culture.

Let me expand a bit and anticipate parts of my later argument. Each culture has systematic properties. Every isolated aspect of a culture, or almost every aspect, is somehow related to every other aspect in ways that may be direct and apparent on the one hand or circuitous on the other. Moreover, these relations have a form or an order. Cultures have organization as well as content. This organization has a variety of limiting conditions such as its economic base or its pervasive principles of social organization. Some cultural traits are simply not compatible with others. But features that experience and analysis show as setting up limits also set directions: goals or values. Or, to make a more cautious assertion, certain dominant cultural features have been found to be more frequently associated with some values than with others. One does not here need to beg questions of causation on one side or the other. My point is that in any event a knowledge of the scaled cluster of values that is distinctive of a given culture is very useful in deciding what discontinuities are significant.

The whole issue, however, remains troublesome. Anthropologists are sure that valid propositions can be constructed about whole cultures that will not emerge from any seriatim listing of parts. They will deny that the problem of deciding "What is a distinct culture?" can correctly be put in the form: "*How many* differences must there be?" They may reply: "It may be only one. It may be quite a number. It all depends on the total configuration." Some, like myself, may add: "The value system is crucial." It must be granted that the whole state of anthropological theory in this respect is vague, fluid, and highly unsatisfactory. Having admitted this, let me turn back to further remarks about the regularities with which cultural anthropologists are concerned.

These embrace behavior, including, of course, verbal behavior, and the products of behavior (artifacts, codified myths, artistic expressions, and so on). Behavior is observed for its sequences, tempo, and periodicities; for its incidences and distributions by age, sex, and other roles. Style (emphasis, intensity, and the like) is noted. Behavioral products are analyzed with reference to observed behavior and as sources of information on technologies and motor habits; discriminative choices of materials, as evidencing degree of knowledge of the natural world and attitudes toward nature; and stylistic and aesthetic bents. The recurrent "choices," manifested in behavior and in the products of behavior, are taken as evidence as to which values are most pervasive and what is their rank order. Verbal behavior is studied as is any other behavior sequence but, in addition, as bases of models for: (a) what people say they do; (b) what they say they ought to do. The anthropologist aims at the eventual construction of three modalities:

(1) of actual behavior and behavioral products;

(2) of the images individuals have of themselves and others as behaving in the context of this culture;

(3) of conceptions of ideal or desirable behavior in existent or hypothetical situations.

In other words, one needs to deal with regularities on three dimensions: in actuality, in expectation on the part of participants, and in the optative mode.

From this brief catalogue, one can easily derive in broad outline what the anthropologist does to depict the "parts" of a culture. He watches which individuals do what in what sequence and for how long. He tries to be alert for what they might do and might well be motivated to do, but in fact, seldom or never do. He listens to what they say and makes notes on some of what fails to be said. In one way or another—he may need to introduce projective tests or crudely experimental situations—he elicits from them their views as to what actually goes on in their society and their notions of what is right and good, wrong and unsatisfying, proper and improper. He collects linguistic texts. He learns what he can from artifacts and other interventions into the nonhuman world. He may well use photographic and other recording devices.

In his description of "parts" the anthropologist pays as careful attention to form as to content. Let me give two examples from linguistic culture. I have conducted hundreds of interviews with Navahos on the subject of witchcraft—a topic they will not ordinarily discuss until good rapport has been established, and even then only after various preliminaries. It is striking that all except about 3 per cent of the individuals uttered, early in the *first* interview in which they actually talked about witchcraft, a sentence that may be literally translated as "I don't know—I just heard about it." Now the content, which is approximately a denial of direct knowledge of witchcraft, could have been expressed in all sorts of words, arranged in a variety of ways. Yet the use of a single form is an almost exceptionless uniformity.

A similar phenomenon is observed when Navahos translate into English. For instance, when the content is that a person ought to avoid particular human beings, animals, or objects, the strongly preferred English verb is "bother" or "bother with." "Don't bother your wife" (usually with the meaning: don't have sexual intercourse with your wife). Similarly, "Young boys shouldn't bother the girls." When a helper in a ceremonial was being sent out to gather plants, a part of the instructions given him was translated: "Then bring them right back—don't bother horses, sheep, or herders on the way." "Avoid" is admittedly too literary a word to expect as a translation, but "keep away from," "don't go near," and other phrases would be congruent with the English vocabularies of the interpreters in question. One does indeed hear these phrases, too, but far more rarely than "bother." Since the interpreters come from widely separated areas of the Navaho country, went to different schools, or learned their English while working for or with whites, the preference for "bother" must be considered a *formal* cultural regularity.

The only constraints set upon the anthropologists' assembling items of behavior, behavioral products, expectations, and standards for behavior are the powerful ones of time and other resources. Yet the sheer corpus of detail upon some nonliterate cultures, to say nothing of civilizations having written languages, is massive. There are longitudinal studies going through twenty-five years and more. There are the published reports of research teams with separate volumes on kinship, basketry, folklore, child training, economy, music, ethnobotany, ethnoentomology, and almost every topic that can be imagined. In the favorable case, each of these monographs may make a contribution to topical generalization and to theory. But as a series of contributions to the depiction of a total culture the bulk is so huge as to be virtually useless to the investigator who wishes to compare whole cultures. Only the specialist who gives his whole research life to consideration of this tribe can wade through and half master the culture-parts described. Such "Sears and Roebuck Catalogue Ethnology," as it is sometimes called, may be monumental and helpful to those who like to pillage such storehouses for the picturesque detail or for items to be lifted out of their contexts and included in lists of distributions of traits or used in statistical manipulations. Clearly, however, the data are not even half-processed.

In fact, to be sure, at least a faltering first step toward generalization has ordinarily been taken in the kind of research report to which I have referred. Raw data are seldom published in extenso—though some of my colleagues feel they should be so published more often. For the most part, the anthropologist will cite the actually observed detail of behavior only to illustrate in the concrete or to document a point of variation or deviation. Most of his utterances will be cast in such formulas as the following which patently are at varying levels of generality and specificity:

Hopi culture enjoins quiet, peaceful conduct.

Almost all Hopis look down upon Navahos.

Young, unmarried Hopi men sleep in "kivas," ceremonial chambers.

Most of my informants (. . . most of my older informants . . .) stated that educated, that is, English-speaking or school-trained, Hopis had little ceremonial knowledge.

I encountered seven individuals who had made the trip to the

Sacred Salt Lake (Better: out of——individuals of such and such ages and sexes whom I interviewed, seven said they had been to the Salt Lake).

Thirty-four per cent out of a total adult female population of 216 still wore woven sashes on the four sample occasions on which I systematically observed for this behavior.

In brief, what is usually reported is a modality of or for behavior. There is great variation in the extent to which minor as well as major modes are indicated and supported by evidence. There are likewise few generally accepted or adhered to standards as to how fully the transgressions of the modal patterns and individual variability and deviation should be documented. Moreover, it must be confessed, anthropologists have not been very consistent in submitting to public scrutiny the variable bases for their postulations of modalities. There are types of cultural information, to be sure, where overdocumentation would be pedantry. As a foreign observer, I do not need many observations to establish such points as the doffing of hats to women under various circumstances or the fact that "I ain't" is not considered to be "good English." If one knows the position of the behaving individuals in the cultural structure, one can validly posit a cultural mode on the basis of sensible observation of a very small sample. On the other hand, when one moves from overt and relatively clear-cut action-sequences to more elusive spheres such as conceptions of nature, attitudes, and values, there is required a more explicit specification of the evidential ground upon which a proposition rests. Did all Zunis with whom one talked say in so many words that their ancestors are clouds and return to the Zuni village as such? How many is "all"? Or was this statement elicited from only two or three persons—and each of these an elderly man? Is this belief in its articulate form a part of Zuni culture only in the sense that "reality is process" is part of our contemporary culture as regards a tiny minority of intellectuals?

But, however inadequate the workmanship of anthropologists in informing their readers as to the basis in fact for the assertion of various modalities may be, it is reasonably clear how one can proceed from the welter of discrete items to first-order abstractions, to the formulation of properly qualified central tendencies and minor modes of second or third order. This still hardly takes us to "whole cultures" about which anthropologists talk rather too glibly. After all, one has moved only from a catalogue of items to a list of modalities that remain unconnected except possibly by apperception.

Yet anthropologists have a stubborn conviction that the interrelation of the modalities ought to be reducible to a comparatively small number of thematic principles. Whence the argument for such a conviction? Language is a part of culture—indeed it is that aspect which most nearly approaches "pure culture." Moreover, it so happens that linguistics is that branch of cultural anthropology where some basic units comparable to elementary particles or genes have been isolated and where analysis of some rigor and genuine elegance has been created. And in that phase of linguistic culture known as phonology it has been demonstrated that a small number of principles called "distinctive features" operate again and again, resonating throughout the system.

It seems justifiable to take the premises that there is a discoverable order in nature, that culture is a part of nature, that it is particularly likely that similar principles will prevail in different aspects of that general category of nature termed culture. Complications can be anticipated, to be sure. In language there is a much more immediate correlation between receptor and effector systems than in other types of cultural behavior. Ordinary linguistic behavior has almost the automatic character of "instinctive" action. The selection and articulation of the phonemes of one's native language is seldom interfered with by conscious reflection.

Nevertheless, it seems reasonable to search in nonlinguistic culture for least common factors or highest common denominators of the sort that we encounter in language. Such thematic principles will, of course, be second-order abstractions, inferential constructs. A sophisticated informant not only can be very articulate about what is correct and incorrect pronunciation, but also can go on to express rules as to what sounds can begin or end an utterance. But an informant without technical training in linguistics can *never* say

"These are the phonemes of our language, and they configurate in this way." The system is the construct of the linguist.

This is a paradigm of what cultural anthropologists mean by "implicit culture"—that is, those stylized ways of thinking, feeling, and reacting that cut across a variety of content categories. They are pervasive, and they are inevitably very abstract. Participants in the culture have no conscious* (that is, verbalizable) awareness of them—any more than of the distinctive features of the phonology. Nevertheless, a parsimonious model of a culture must be constructed in considerable part from these implicit, thematic features. Only thus can one give information about a culture that will tend to make all additional information redundant or predictable.

On the other hand, an adequate description of the distinctiveness of a whole-culture will ordinarily involve elements that range through the spectrum from completely explicit to completely implicit. The anthropologist's formulation of these elements is likely to be more condensed, more compressed than generalizations made by participants in the culture. He may condense into a single statement ostensibly divergent cultural utterances that seem to him reducible to a single underlying theme, a common element of meaning. Yet there will be much in his construct that is easily identifiable in terms of the overt culture. Reasonably articulate informants when confronted with the model will say of those portions that immediately reflect the explicit culture, "Yes, that is the way we believe, the way we think."

Karl Pribram has said that the primate nervous system is a vast tautology, a tissue of redundancies. The same may be said of any culture. How can one cut through the redundancies, best combining maximal information with brevity? I am sure that exposure of the

* There is no implication whatsoever that the implicit culture is, as it were, present in the unconscious (in the psychoanalytic sense) of participants. I mean only that of those rules of the game that make up a culture some can be stated more easily and fully by those who share that culture than others. Implicit culture is the unstated, unannounced part. It is that aspect which is most taken-for-granted, unquestioned. One may even speculate that implicit culture is that sector of coherence in whole-culture where individuals are most comfortable. Cognitive explicitness in personal behavior is often a symptom of strain and attended with symptoms of compulsiveness.

core values of a culture and their hierarchical interrelations reveals at least as much as any other single analytic operation about the structural essence of each culture. My wife[1] and I[2] have suggested ways of defining the distinctive value-profiles of cultures. But for an over-all model of the forms in which part-culture is put together into whole-culture something more is necessary. I suspect that there are three indispensable requirements:

(1) *Salient Categories.* Which categories are used most frequently to order experience? Do some categories have a kind of evident primacy, either in the sense that they are ultimate and not discussible or in the sense that many other categories can be shown to be merely group-specified subsets of a more embracing concept? The major categories may be named in the lexicon or they may be crypto-categories (that is, features of the implicit culture). If the culturally distinctive categories are named, they are likely to present peculiar difficulties in rendering the terms into another language.

(2) *Existential Premises.* How is the world and experience in it conceived? What forms of relatedness are held to exist between events? What inexorable limits does nature, including human nature, put upon the satisfaction of human desires and aspirations?

(3) *Evaluative Premises.* What are the the final standards of the right and the good?

Specification of these points may give the beginnings of a cultural topology: a geometry of forms that lack size and definite, easily describable shape. Certainly the realm of culture is one of those which Warren Weaver[3] has characterized as "problems of organized complexity."

Rather than elaborating further an abstract consideration of the search for ordering principles that may make possible the characterization of whole-culture, I propose to give an illustration. If in the next few pages I attempted to sketch the structure (that is, the order or arrangement of parts) in Navaho culture as a totality, the result would be too thin. I can give some body to the sketch by centering upon one sector of the culture, the "religious," though I shall not restrict myself exclusively to this. In fact—as ought to be the case if the theory I have outlined is at all correct—the premises and categories, both explicit and implicit, that give general form to the religious sphere may be detected either palpably or as submerged configurations in all or most of the recurrent cultural regularities of Navaho life. "Religion" is not a subdivision of the culture that can be neatly sliced out but rather an aspect of the total culture. But, if one focuses upon beliefs and practices that in Navaho culture are associated with the supernatural, the pertinent data come down to fairly manageable dimensions.

PART-CULTURE AND WHOLE-CULTURE IN NAVAHO RELIGION

Navaho ideas about the supernatural and Navaho ritual behaviors constitute an exceedingly complex and ramified system. There is the corpus of beliefs and practices that relates to witchcraft. There are the long myths that provide the warrant for ceremonials and detail the origin of the world, of man, of the Navaho people, and of the various clans. There are folktales which refer to supernatural matters. There are rites of divination, of girls' puberty, of war, of blessing and consecration. There are major ceremonials to cure illness. There are numberless exoteric rites of the daily life of the individual and the family. Rituals have also been incorporated into agriculture, trading, hunting, and gathering.

The question is: Can many bits of religious ideas and of ceremonial behavior be shown to be a partial expression of one or more of a much smaller number of principles that pervade the whole system? Are the same combinations or linkages, the same modes of categorizing, inferring, and relating found in all the subsystems? Can the same concept, or event, or class of concept or event be shown to be derivable from more than one of the basic categories or principles? The only valid test of the exposition which follows would be if the reader, scanning for the first time a Navaho myth or seeing a ceremony, knew what to expect next—beyond chance concatenation and beyond generalized knowledge of human nature. If my account is roughly valid, then the reader should be able to predict certain sequences, anticipate some kinds of symbolic accoutrements and not others, expect one kind of detail and not another, foresee this sort of rationalization as opposed to that.

Let me start with some statements that are concrete yet general. Ceremonial behavior, including ceremonial discourse, is differentiated from nonceremonial behavior and is prescribed in minutely orderly fashion. Thus, only food for ceremonial occasions may be stirred with a single stick. This food must always be stirred in a clockwise direction. Certain isolable parts always recur in ritual events: prayers and songs that contain repetitive locutions, offerings, purifications (by sweating, emetics, and the like), restrictions upon the behavior of participants (continence, urination at only certain times and places, sleeping only at certain times and places), avoidances (for instance, of menstrual blood), and designated ritual locales. There are many detailed variations of these prescriptions and many permutations and combinations of them, but the same identifiable entities always recur.

From them alone one might hazard deductions as to ordering principles, some of which are familiar from many cultures:

(1) The distinction between the sacred and the profane;
(2) The prizing of repetitive order;
(3) A lively sense of the dangers in human behavior;
(4) More specifically, a fear of the risks attendant upon human bodily functions and hence a need for control.

But I think we shall get further if we proceed more systematically, following the scheme of salient categories, existential premises, and evaluative premises.

Salient Categories

"The act" I take to be the most fundamental Navaho category. There is no single Navaho noun for this summative concept—partly because Navaho is overwhelmingly a verbal language. Substantives and qualities are definitely secondary. Persons (actors) are prominent in Navaho discourse but far less stressed than their actions. It is very difficult in Navaho to make fine distinctions as to attributes.

But when one talks of events such as "going" it is obligatory to make at least a hundred discriminations.

John Ladd says:

> . . . casual power varies with ability to travel. If a being is capable of getting somewhere in practically no time, he is extremely powerful. Hence, the emphasis on the capacity of the various divinities to travel back and forth at tremendous speeds. The potency of thunder, lightning, and whirlwinds may be explained on this principle. Ghosts and witches are thought to be capable of roaming at great speed. It would seem that ability to travel is a necessary adjunct of power, and consequently of dangerousness.[4]

The only Navaho word that comes even close to English "rite" means approximately: "something is being done." The Navaho distinguish the various kinds of witchcraft only by their techniques: what is being done. When divination is practiced there are only two questions asked: how did this happen? what can be done to repair the damage or avert an impending calamity? The myths are always centered upon events rather than philosophical speculation or vague, literary imaginings: who went where? who did what? what happened next? Mythological explanations are always directed to acts, accomplished or potential.

Ritual behavior is neither spontaneous nor based upon a generalized and abstract calculus nor calendrical. It is always precipitated by an immediate event: birth, puberty, illness, war, the hunt, death. Deviant belief is never regarded as a religious transgression. If such belief does lead to an error in action, it is the act that must be corrected—not the conception. Motor behavior is significant rather than verbal adherence to a theological or ethical code.

In a paper[5] published since the above paragraphs were written, Herbert Landar notes that the theme of motionful activity is central in these stories—that it is crucial in solving problems such as getting property. He also points out that motifs of action (especially motion) are considerably more prominent in Navaho Rorschachs than in those of three other Southwestern groups (Zuni Indians, Spanish-Americans, Mormons).

Location. The position of every person, animal, and object is most elaborately specified in every domain of Navaho religion. The myths stating the residences of the supernatural beings, and their movements—and those of all of the *dramatis personae*—are detailed so minutely as to be boring to the non-Navaho. This almost obsessive preoccupation with precise specification represents, of course, a linkage of the categories of action and location. Position, indeed, seems defined by the Navaho as the resultant of the withdrawal of motion (action).

The basic dichotomy of "Holy People" (supernaturals) and "Earth Surface People" (humans) rests upon a spatial distinction. The spirits of different kinds of dead are believed to go to different regions. Spatial arrangements are rigidly prescribed in all forms of ceremonial. The patient must sit in a particular place and the ceremonialist in another. One side of the hut is for men, the other for women. There is a fixed ritual order for all movement. Each color is associated with one of the cardinal directions. Plants used in a rite must be gathered in the east or from the north side of a tree. Ceremonial objects and the remains of a destroyed sandpainting must be deposited in particular places or in particular directions.

This tendency goes so far that "time" is almost assimilated to the category of space. Navaho verbs have many aspects and voices, but there are only two rudimentary tenses, indicated by enclitics. Time as duration is virtually absent from Navaho thinking. But time as a sequence of events is well developed. The order of acts in a ceremonial must be rigorously followed, and any deviation demands repetition of the sequence or of the whole ceremony in correct order. An actual reversal is prima facie indication of witchcraft. In mythology the stress is always upon the sequential pattern of events. The Navaho thus in their whole-culture—and not least in their religion—treat time in terms of "before" and "after," thus reducing it to a sort of spatial arrangement. And note once more that the reference point is a series of "eventings."

Another outcome of the insistence upon location is that every subjective experience must have its correlate, which is placed definitely in the sense world. It is not enough, for instance, for a Navaho to say " I *know* I am being witched." He (or his relatives) must point to tracks at a given location or must affirm that dirt was dislodged from a particular place on the hogan roof during the night. Many other types of located event can be specified: a person who is thought to be hostile to the "victim" has allegedly been seen near a grave. But witchcraft anxiety and fear become credible only when associated with a combination of event and location.

Complementarity. This category is prominent but not quite as pervasive as those of action and location. "Earth Surface People" and "Holy People" exhaust between them the totality of the personalized. All of experience is divided into the sacred and the profane, although only the former category is unequivocally represented in the vocabulary of the language. The "good side" and the "bad side" (as English-speaking Navahos put it) of the religion are necessary, one to the other. In spite of the fact that witchcraft is defined as the worst crime, the "good ceremonialist must know some witchcraft—else he would go dry." The Navaho oppose prophylactic rites ("Blessing Way" and related ceremonies) to curing chants (where a rattle is employed). Yet every curing chant must have its "Blessing Way part."

The balance of opposites is an essential part of the stable order of the world. The sun and moon are so conceived. Similarly, the sacred mountain in the north is balanced with that of the south, and the east with the west. (Here and elsewhere in the cultural system we have a junction of the categories of location and complementarity.) Maleness and femaleness are so necessarily complementary that the contrast is carried far beyond the animal realm. There are male and female rains, lightnings, turquoise, and ceremonials. Each male divinity has a female counterpart in a dry painting.

At the psychological level this duality of the sexes probably signifies the complementary nature of stronger and weaker, dominant and submissive. Similarly, as Spencer[6] has shown in her very thorough analysis of the myths of chants, the Navaho conceive of the development of independence as containing both beneficent and aggressive-destructive components. This is a specific manifestation of a wider paradigm: Evil and good are complementary and both are ever-present (in the gods, in men, in "natural forces").

The pairing of older and younger doubtless has also latent psychological elements as well as reflecting the positional category.

Mirroring Navaho kinship terminology, some of the divinities appear in pairs of elder and younger siblings.

Personality. The Navaho have a strong tendency to invest all phenomena with the attributes of personality. This is more than simple and classic "animism." Each plant and each animal have *both* a plant or animal form *and* a human form. They can remove one or the other at will. The "man form" is held to be indestructible.

The sun is at once a physical body and "day carrier in space." The moon is a mass and also "night carrier in space." There are "star people," "wind people," "cloud people," and the like. All natural phenomena are taken possession of by "one who lies within it." This "inner form" is independent of the object which it happens to occupy.

The ubiquity of this personalizing concept has two main consequences in Navaho religious thought and action: (1) the universe and all experience are humanized; (2) the ground is laid for possible interconnections between any object or event and any human action.

Immunity. This category can be properly regarded as a special case of "complementarity" (in its sacred vs. profane aspect) but is distinctive enough for Navaho culture to discuss separately. The supernaturals are the *diyin* People. *Diyin* is ordinarily translated into English as "Holy." This is unfortunate because no connotation of moral sanctity is involved in the term. Rather, it conveys that the divinities are immune to disease and injury. Under certain circumstances "Earth Surface People" (humans) can acquire a limited "immunity." The ceremonialist who has learned a myth and the accompanying rite can safely act as an intermediary between divinities and men. So long as he is carrying out a ritual that he has mastered he is "immune." The patient in a ceremonial becomes identified with the supernaturals involved in it and is thereafter immune to attack from those particular divinities.

Existential Premises

(1) *Every event has its consequences.* There are no "accidents" to the Navaho. If not a mechanist, he is certainly a deter-

minist. This premise is fundamental to all Navaho religious behavior. The generic term for a transgression that needs ritual remedy can best be translated "one took a chance"—that is, a person acted in the face of the realization that human life is governed by an ineluctable connection between act and result. The supernaturals are likewise bound by the rules.

Religious transgressions bring the same penalties whether willful violation of the rules was involved or mere ignorance and error. Problems for the eminently practical Navaho resolve themselves into two forms: if I do this (fail to do this), what will happen? which event in the chain is responsible for my present illness or misfortune, and what acts are best calculated to correct the causal sequence and restore order? Recourse to the categories of action, location, complementarity, and personality is involved in answering these questions.

(2) *Evil and danger are immanent in experience.* If every event has its consequence and if the universe is built out of the complementarity of opposites, it follows that things can go wrong—and, not infrequently, very wrong. This the Navaho has learned from his daily life where serious illness and accident, hunger, and actual starvation are witnessed again and again. But he links this induction from direct experience to his existential premise of the lawful relatedness of events as they are juxtaposed in "before" and "after" sequences. Hence the Navaho, even more than many nonliterate peoples, honor the logic of *post hoc, ergo propter hoc.*

(3) *Knowledge is power.* This premise could properly, from the Navaho viewpoint, be linked to the foregoing one by the adversative, "but." The Navaho is no serene or acceptant "fatalist." Given the centrality of the category of "action" in Navaho culture, he could hardly be. Rather, he operates on the premise that, since acts do possess a determinate relatedness rather than a haphazard distribution, the course of events can be manipulated if one knows how.

The Navaho is a utilitarian and values all knowledge that he deems useful. The technological skills of agriculture, of hunting, of arts and crafts, are all prized. Property is highly valued by the

Navaho, and secular knowledge is highly relevant to the accumulation of property. Possessions as well as ceremonial knowledge are useful in the ritual control of events. Yet, in Navaho opinion the most powerful technology is that of religion itself. Through religious knowledge events may be foreseen, disaster may be averted, and illness may be cured. Divination can reveal the etiology of misfortune, and this information suggests the ceremonial acts to be undertaken in order to right the causative linkage of events. Correct knowledge makes possible the restoration of harmony in family relations and indeed in the universe as a whole.

Complete knowledge is unattainable. What is possessed, however, is an inalienable good. It can coerce even supernatural beings. If the right procedures are followed, the divinities *must* restore the patient to health and harmonious living. The conception of "good luck" is hard to translate into the Navaho language. One has the requisite knowledge (sacred or profane) or one hasn't. Even in what European languages call "games of chance" the Navaho depends upon medicines, rites, and verbal formulas. The same is true with hunting. Getting a deer is not a matter of good fortune; it depends upon ritual knowledge and one's (controllable) relations with the supernaturals. Knowledge, for the Navaho, is always defined as: how to act.

Navaho culture holds to other existential premises such as the virtually pan-human principles of sympathetic ("like produces like") and holophrastic ("part stands for whole")[7] magic. The way in which these and other familiar assumptions gear into the salient Navaho categories and premises has, of course, its own specific dimensions. But I believe that the three premises listed and briefly discussed are those which, in their combinations, are distinctive for Navaho culture.

Evaluative Premises

(1) *Harmony is the ultimate value.* This means the elimination of friction in human relations. It means the absence of interference with natural and lawful processes. For example, the living

of a long and healthy life is an instance of "harmony" in the Navaho sense. In the physical world an eclipse is an illustration of "disharmony." The premise implies balance, including the complementarity of contrasting entities. It implies control and regulation.

All ceremonials are directed primarily toward the restoration of harmony in that total economy of things of which human affairs constitute only one facet. In the Navaho conception of the relationships, among their divinities there is a notion of a balance of opposing forces. No one divine being has unfettered control over the others. Each is limited by the powers of the others as well as by the remorseless working out of processes beyond the control of the whole pantheon.

In this equilibrium of forces human effort in the form of observance of taboos and in the performance of compulsive rituals can play its part. Individually acquired knowledge can assist in the restoration of harmony in one person's life, in that of the group, and in that of the whole universe.

The striving for balance is reflected in the scrupulous symmetry of ceremonial-parts, mythic narratives, and ceremonial art. Ritual poetry is constructed in the fugue and coda style. Prayers contain numberless balanced repetitions, four being the favorite pattern. All of the religious symbolism has the latent content: each portion is related to the rest; all are necessary; harmony consists in the appropriate relatedness of each portion to every other portion; order is the final virtue.

Illness is one price of disorder. Death before ripe old age is another. Health and long life must to some degree be goals in all societies that maintain themselves. In the Navaho case they are accentuated the more because there is no thought of happiness in or preparation for a future life. The relevant point here is that disease is always traced back to disorder rather than to what Europeans consider "natural causes." Even a broken limb from an "accident" has its etiology in some disharmony. The outward and visible form of the disharmony may be a disturbance in human relations, but this, in turn, is the manifestation of malequilibrium in the sufferer's relations to the total order of the world. The individual, the social group, the supernaturals, and the rest of the animate and inanimate universe are all part of one scheme. Anything that disturbs the balance of this system as a whole can produce malfunctioning in any part of the system. The symptom may be an "accident," a physiological lesion, social friction, lack of rainfall, or a flood.

(2) *Knowledge and effort are good.* This value-premise is almost inevitably consequent upon the three existential premises. In part, it also flows from the first evaluative premise because skill and work can promote harmony. However, to the Navaho, action based upon knowledge also produces immediate benefits that are not directly referable to the harmony principle. On the other hand, the remaining value-premises are all corollaries of the evaluation of harmony.

(3) *Control of oneself and indeed of everything is necessary.* This premise (and the frequently heard Navaho negative: "avoid excess") follow naturally upon the preoccupation with action (or inhibition of action) and upon the conviction that, since events are determinate, the course of things can be influenced.

Sobriety and adherence to the old customs of Navaho religious behavior are valued. It is shameful for a Navaho family to lack a sweathouse. To respect the ceremonials and to carry them out in orderly fashion helps to maintain stability and regularity. "Control" means to support order.

(4) *Reciprocity is a cardinal virtue.* No society can survive unless its culture prescribes rewards for reciprocal behavior. This is heavily stressed in Navaho culture, especially as regards reciprocal obligations between relatives. "Act toward everyone as if he were your relative" is the widest Navaho morality.

In the religious sphere such general benevolence is subordinated to expectable patterns of behavior between kinsmen. If your siblings and your clan relatives attend ceremonials in your immediate family, you must attend theirs—and equal the gifts and services they have provided. The myths are replete with injunctions to observe reciprocal obligations and with models for such behavior. This value-premise seems closely connected with the category of complementarity.

The above listing may be compared with Spencer's (op. cit., p. 86) results from an exhaustive study of the chant-myths:

> The value themes identified in plot construction center in four areas: the maintenance of health; the acquisition of supernatural power; the maintenance of harmony in family relationships; and the process of the young man's attainment of adult status.

My listing, based as it is upon ritual acts and verbal material not analyzed by Spencer, has greater generality. And all of Spencer's points save one are either explicit or implicit in my treatment. What is missing is the emphasis upon the male's acquisition of responsible and controlled behavior.

SUMMARY

We have, then, an oversimplified and sparsely documented but still, I think, instructive representation of structural principles which cut across a variety of discrete areas of content in Navaho religious culture:

Salient Categories: action, location, complementarity, immunity
Existential Premises: determinateness, evil-danger, knowledge-power
Evaluative Premises: harmony, knowledge-effort, control, reciprocity

One may derive from their mutual constraints and positive forwardings a great deal of what in fact prevails in Navaho lore and behavior.

NOTES

1. Florence Kluckhohn and Fred Strodtbeck, *Variations in Value Orientations,* Evanston, Ill.: Row, Peterson, and Co., 1960.
2. Clyde Kluckhohn, "The Scientific Study of Values," in *University of Toronto Installation Lectures,* Toronto: University of Toronto Press, 1958.
3. Warren Weaver, "Science and Complexity," *American Scientist,* 36:536–44 (1948).
4. John Ladd, *The Structure of a Moral Code,* Cambridge, Mass.: Harvard University Press, 1956, p. 221.

5. Herbert Landar, "Four Navaho Summer Tales," *Journal of American Folklore*, 72:298–309.

6. Katherine Spencer, *Mythology and Values, Memoirs of the American Folklore Society*, Vol. 48; 1957.

7. The same word is used to designate a medicine bundle with all its contents, the contents of the bundle, and any separate item of these contents.

Wholes, Sums, and Organic Unities*

Ernest Nagel

In connection with the subject of reduction and emergence, it is helpful to discuss a familiar notion that is frequently associated with these themes. According to this notion there occurs in nature an important type of individual wholes (which may be physical, biological, psychological, or social) that are not simply "aggregates" of independent members, but are "organic unities"; and such wholes are often characterized by the familiar dictum that they possess an organization which makes each of them "more than the sum of its parts." Examples of wholes that are "organic," and that allegedly also illustrate this dictum, can be cited from many fields of inquiry. Since such alleged facts are sometimes taken as indications of limits to the possibility of reduction and to the scope of the methods of the physical sciences, it is instructive to consider them with some care. And in the course of examining them we shall be compelled to recognize distinctions that will be useful in the sequel.

The first point to note, however, is that words like "whole" and "sum" as commonly employed are unusually vague, ambiguous, and even metaphorical; and until their senses are clarified, it is frequently impossible to assess the worth of statements containing them. Let us make this evident by an example. A quadrilateral encloses an area, and either one of its diameters divides it into two partial areas whose sum is equal to the area of the whole figure. In this and many analogous contexts the statement "The whole is equal to the sum of its parts" is usually said to be not only true, but ***necessarily*** true, so that its denial is commonly regarded as self-contradictory. On the other hand, some writers have maintained, on com-

* Reprinted from *Philosophical Studies* III, 2 (February 1952).

paring the taste of sugar or lead with the taste of its chemical components, that in this case the whole is not equal to the sum of its parts. Now this assertion is intended to supply some information about the matters discussed; and it cannot be rejected without further ado as simply a logical absurdity. It is clear, therefore, that in this latter context the words "whole," "part," and "sum" (and perhaps "equal") are being employed in senses different from those associated with them in the previous context. We must therefore assume the task of distinguishing between a number of senses of these words that appear to play a role in various inquiries.

1. *Wholes and parts.* The words "whole" and "part" are normally used for correlative distinctions, so that x is said to be a whole in relation to something y which is a component or part of x in some sense or other. It will be convenient, therefore, to have before us a brief list of certain familiar "kinds" of wholes and corresponding parts.

a. The word "whole" is used to refer to something with a spatial extension, and anything is then called a "part" of such a whole that is spatially included in it. However, there are several special senses of "whole" and "part" that fall under this head. In the first place, they may refer to specifically spatial properties, so that the whole is then some length, area, or volume that contains as parts lengths, areas, or volumes. In this sense, neither wholes nor parts need be spatially continuous—thus, the United States and its territorial possessions are not a spatially continuous whole, which contains as one of its spatial parts the desert regions, which are also not spatially continuous. In the second place, "whole" may refer to a nonspatial property or state of a spatially extended thing, and "part" designates an identical property of some spatial part of the thing. Thus, the electric charge on a body is said to have for its parts the electric charges on spatial parts of the body. In the third place, though sometimes only such spatial properties are counted as parts of a spatial whole that have the same spatial dimensions as the latter, at other times the usage is more liberal. Thus, the surface of a sphere is frequently said to be a part of the sphere, even if on other occasions only volumes in the sphere's interior are so designated.

b. The word "whole" refers to some temporal period, whose

parts are temporal intervals in it. As in the case of spatial wholes and parts, temporal ones need not be continuous.

c. The word "whole" refers to any class, set, or aggregate of elements, and "part" may then designate either any proper subclass of the initial set or any element in the set. Thus, by a part of the whole consisting of all the books printed in the United States during a given year may be understood either all the novels printed that year, or some particular copy of a novel.

d. The word "whole" sometimes refers to a property of an object or process, and "part" to some analogous property that stands to the first in certain specified relations. Thus, a force in physics is commonly said to have for its parts or components other forces into which the first can be analyzed according to a familiar rule. Similarly, the physical brightness of a surface illuminated by two sources of light is sometimes said to have for one of its parts the brightness associated with one of the sources. In the present sense of the words, a part is not a spatial part of the whole.

e. The word "whole" may refer to a pattern of relations between certain specified kinds of objects or events, the pattern being capable of embodiment on various occasions and with various modifications. However, "part" may then designate different things in different contexts. It may refer to any one of the elements that are related in that pattern on some occasion of its embodiment. Thus, if a melody (say "Auld Lang Syne") is such a whole, one of its parts is then the first tone that is sounded when the melody is sung on a particular date. Or it may refer to a class of elements that occupy corresponding positions in the pattern in some specified mode of its embodiment. Thus, one of the parts of the melody will then be the class of first notes when "Auld Lang Syne" is sung in the key of G minor. Or the word "part" may refer to a subordinate pattern in the total one. In this case, a part of the melody will be the pattern of tones that occurs in its first four bars.

f. The word "whole" may refer to a process, one of its parts being another process that is some discriminated phase of the more inclusive one. Thus, the process of swallowing is part of the process of eating.

g. The word "whole" may refer to any concrete object, and

"part" to any of its properties. In this sense, the character of being cylindrical in shape or being malleable is a part of a given piece of copper wire.

h. Finally, the word "whole" is often used to refer to any system whose spatial parts stand to each other in various relations of dynamical dependence. Many of the so-called organic unities appear to be systems of this type. However, in the present sense of "whole" a variety of things are customarily designated as its parts. Thus, a system consisting of a mixture of two gases inside a container is frequently, though not always in the same context, said to have for its parts one or more of the following: its spatially extended constituents, such as the two gases and the container; the properties or states of the system or of its spatial parts, such as the mass of the system or the specific heats of one of the gases; the processes that the system undergoes in reaching or maintaining thermodynamical equilibrium; and the spatial or dynamical organization to which its spatial parts are subject.

This list of senses of "whole" and "part," though by no means complete, will suffice to indicate the ambiguity of these words. But what is more important, it also suggests that since the word "sum" is used in a number of contexts in which these words occur, it suffers from an analogous ambiguity. Let us therefore examine several of its typical senses.

2. *Senses of "sum."* We shall not inquire whether the word "sum" actually is employed in connection with each of the senses of "whole" and "part" that have been distinguished, and if so just what meaning is to be associated with it. In point of fact, it is not easy to specify a clear sense for the word in many contexts in which people do use it. We shall accordingly confine ourselves to noting only a small number of the well-established uses of "sum," and to suggesting interpretations for it in a few contexts in which its mean- is unclear and its use misleading.

a. It is hardly surprising that the most carefully defined uses of "sum" and "addition" occur in mathematics and formal logic. But even in these contexts the word has a variety of special meanings, depending on what type of mathematical and logical "objects" are being added. Thus, there is a familiar operation of addition for the natural integers; and there are also identically named but really distinct operations for ratios, real numbers, complex numbers, matrices, classes, relations and other "entities." It is not altogether evident why all these operations have the common name of "addition," though there are at least certain formal analogies between many of them—for example, most of them are commutative and associative. However, there are some important exceptions to the general rule implicit in this example, for the addition of *ordered* sets is not uniformly commutative, though it is associative. On the other hand, the sum of two entities is invariably some unique entity, which is of the same type as the summands—thus, the sum of two integers is an integer, of two matrices a matrix, and so on. Moreover, though the word "part" is not always defined or used in connection with mathematical "objects," whenever both it and "sum" are employed they are so used that the statement "The whole is equal to the sum of its parts" is an analytic or necessary truth.

However, it is easy to construct an apparent counterinstance to this last claim. Let K^* be the *ordered* set of integers, ordered in the following manner: first the odd integers in order of increasing magnitude, and then the even integers in that order. K^* may then be represented by this notation: $(1, 3, 5, \ldots 2, 4, 6, \ldots)$. Next let K_1 be the class of odd integers and K_2 the class of even ones, neither class being an ordered set. Now let K be the class-sum of K_1 and K_2, so that K contains all the integers as members; K also is not an ordered class. But the membership of K is the same as that of K^*, although quite clearly K and K^* are not identical. Accordingly, so it might be argued, in this case the whole (namely K^*) is not equal to the sum (K) of its parts.

This example is instructive on three counts. It shows that it is possible to define in a precise manner the words "whole," "part," and "sum" so that "The whole is unequal to the sum of its parts" is not only not logically absurd, but is in fact logically true. There is, therefore, no a priori reason for dismissing such statements as inevitable nonsense, and the real issue is to determine, when such an assertion is made, in what sense if any the crucial words in it are being used in the given context. But the example also shows that though such a sentence may be true in one specified usage of "part" and "sum," it may be possible to assign other senses to these words so that the whole *is* equal to the sum of its parts in this redefined sense of the words. Indeed, it is not standard usage in mathematics to call either K_1 or K_2 a part of K^*. On the contrary, it is customary to count as a part of K^* only an ordered segment. Thus, let K_1^* be the ordered set of odd integers arranged according to increasing magnitude, and K_2^* the corresponding ordered set of even integers. K_1^* and K_2^* are then parts of K^*. (K^* has other parts as well; for example, the ordered segments indicated by the following: [1, 3, 5, 7] [9, 11 . . . 2, 4], and [6, 8, . . .].) Now form the ordered sum of K_1^* and K_2^*. But this sum yields the ordered set K^*, so that in the specified senses of "part" and "sum" the whole *is* equal to the sum of its parts. It is thus clear that when a given system has a special type of organization or structure, a *useful* definition of "addition," if such can be given, must take into account that mode of organization. There are any number of operations that could be selected for the label "summation," but not all of them are relevant or appropriate for advancing a given domain of inquiry.

Finally, the example suggests that though a system has a distinctive structure, it is not in principle impossible to specify that structure in terms of relations between its elementary constituents, and moreover in such a manner that the structure can be correctly characterized as a "sum" whose "parts" are themselves specified in terms of those elements and relations. As we shall see, many students deny, or appear to deny, this possibility in connection with certain kinds of organized systems (such as living things). The present example therefore shows that though we may not be able *as a matter of fact* to analyze certain highly complex "dynamic" (or "organic") unities in terms of some given theory concerning their ultimate constituents, such inability cannot be established as a matter of *inherent logical necessity*.

b. If we now turn to the positive sciences, we find that here too there are a large number of well-defined operations called "addition." The major distinction that needs to be drawn is between scalar and vector sums. Let us consider each in turn. Examples of the former are the addition of the numerosity of groups of things, of spatial properties (length, area, and volume), of temporal periods, of weights, of electrical resistance, electric charge, and thermal capacity. They illustrate the first three senses of "whole" and "part" that we distinguished above; and in each of them (and in many other cases that could be mentioned) "sum" is so specified that the whole is the sum of appropriately chosen parts.

On the other hand, there are many magnitudes for which no operation of addition is defined, or seems capable of being defined in any useful manner, such as density or elasticity; most of these cases fall under the last four of the above distinctions concerning "whole" and "part." Moreover, there are some properties for which addition is specified only under highly specialized circumstances; for example, the sum of the brightness of two sources of light is defined only when the light emitted is monochromatic. It makes no sense, therefore, to say that the density (or the shape) of a body is, or is not, the sum of the densities (or shapes) of its parts, simply because there are neither explicitly formulated rules nor ascertainable habits of procedure which associate a usage with the word "sum" in such a context.

The addition of vector properties, such as forces, velocities, and accelerations, conforms to the familiar rule of parallelogram composition. Thus, if a body is acted on by a force of three poundals in a direction due north, and also by a force of four poundals in a direction due east, the body will behave as if it were acted on by a single force of five poundals in a northeasterly direction. This single force is said to be the "sum" or "resultant" of the other two forces, which are called its "components"; and conversely, any force can be analyzed as the sum of an arbitrary number of components. This sense of "sum" is commonly associated with the fourth of the above distinctions concerning "whole" and "part"; and it is evident that here the sense of "sum" is quite different from the sense of the word in such contexts as "the sum of two lengths."

It has been argued by Bertrand Russell that a force cannot rightly be said to be the sum of its components. Thus, he declared:

> Let there be three particles *A, B, C*. We may say that *B* and *C* both cause accelerations in *A*, and we compound these accelerations by the parallelogram law. But this composition is not truly addition, for the components are not *parts* of the resultant. The resultant is a new term, as

simple as their components, and not by any means their sum. Thus the effects attributed to *B* and *C* are never produced, but a third term different from either is produced. This, we may say, is produced by *B* and *C* together, taken as a whole. But the effect which they produce as a whole can only be discovered by supposing each to produce a separate effect: if this were not supposed, it would be impossible to obtain the two accelerations whose resultant is the actual acceleration. Thus we seem to reach an antinomy: the whole has no effect except what results from the effects of the parts, but the effects of the parts are nonexistent.[1]

However, all that this argument shows is that by the component of a force (or of an acceleration) we do not mean anything like what we understand by a component or part of a length—the components of forces are not *spatial parts* of forces. It does not establish the claim that the addition of forces "is not truly addition"—unless, indeed, the word "addition" is being used so restrictively that no operation is to be so designated that does not involve a juxtaposition of spatial (or possibly temporal) parts of the whole said to be their sum. But in this latter event many other operations that are called "addition" in physics, such as the addition of electrical capacities, would also have to receive different labels. Moreover, no antinomy arises from the supposition that, on the one hand, the effect which each component force would produce were it to act alone does not exist, while on the other hand the actual effect produced by the joint action of the components is the resultant of their partial effects. For the supposition simply expresses what is the case, in a language conforming to the antecedent *definition* of the addition and resolution of forces.

The issue raised by Russell is thus terminological at best. His objection is nevertheless instructive. For it calls needed attention to the fact that when the matter is viewed abstractly, the "sum" of a given set of elements is simply an element that is *uniquely determined* by some *function* (in the mathematical sense) of the given set. This function may be assigned a relatively simple and familiar form in certain cases, and a more complex and strange form in others; and in any event, the question whether such a function is to be introduced into a given domain of inquiry, and if so what special form is to be assigned to it, cannot be settled a priori. But the heart of the matter is that when such a function is specified, and if a set of elements satisfy whatever conditions are prescribed by the function, it becomes possible to *deduce* from these premises a class of statements about some structural complex of those elements.[2]

c. We must now consider a use of "sum" that is associated with the fifth sense of "whole" and "part" distinguished above—a use that is also frequently associated with the dictum that the whole is more than, or at any rate not merely, the sum of its parts. Let us assume that the following statement is typical of such usage: "Although a melody may be produced by sounding a series of individual tones on a piano, the melody is not the sum of its individual notes." The obvious question that needs to be asked is: "In what sense is 'sum' being employed here?" It is evident that the statement can be informative only if there *is* such a thing as the sum of the individual tones of melody. For the statement can be established as true or false only if it is possible to compare such a sum with the whole that is the melody.

However, most people who are inclined to assert such a statement do not specify what the sum is supposed to be; and there is, therefore, a basis for the supposition that they either are not clear about what they mean, or do not mean anything whatever. In the latter case the most charitable view that can be taken of such pronouncements is to regard them as simply misleading expressions of the possibly valid claim that the notion of summation is *inapplicable* to the constituent tones of melodies. On the other hand, some writers apparently understand by "sum" in this context the *unordered* class of individual tones; and what they are therefore asserting is that this class is not the melody. But this is hardly news, though conceivably there may have been some persons who believed otherwise. In any event, there appears to be no meaning other than this one which is associated with any regularity with the phrase "sum of tones" or similar phrases. Accordingly, if the word "sum" is used in this sense in contexts in which the word "whole" refers to a pattern or configuration formed by elements standing to each other in certain relations, it is perfectly true, though trivial, to say that the whole is more than the sum of its parts.

As has already been noted, however, this fact does not preclude the possibility of *analyzing* such wholes into a set of elements related to one another in definite ways; nor does it exclude the possibility of assigning a different sense to "sum" so that a melody might then be construed as a sum of appropriately selected parts. It is evident that at least a partial analysis of a melody is effected when it is represented in the customary musical notation; and the analysis could obviously be made more complete and explicit, and even expressed with formal precision.[3]

But it is sometimes maintained in this connection that it is a fundamental mistake to regard the constituent tones of a melody as independent parts, out of which the melody can be reconstituted. On the contrary, it has been argued that what we "experience at each place in the melody is a *part* which is itself determined by the character of the whole. . . . The flesh and blood of a tone depends from the start upon its role in the melody: a *b* as leading tone to *c* is something radically different from the *b* as tonic."[4] And as we shall see, similar views have been advanced in connection with other cases and types of *Gestalts* and "organic" wholes.

Now it may be quite true that the *effect* produced by a given tone depends on its position in a context of other tones, just as the effect produced by a given pressure upon a body is in general contingent upon what other pressures are operative. But this supposed fact does not imply that a melody cannot rightly be viewed as a relational complex whose component tones are identifiable independently of their occurrence in that complex. For if the implication did hold, it would be impossible to describe how a melody is constituted out of individual tones, and therefore impossible to prescribe how it is to be played. Indeed, it would then be self-contradictory to say that "a *b* as leading to *c* is something radically different from the *b* as tonic." For the name "*b*" in the expression "*b* as leading to *c*" could then not refer to the same tone to which the name "*b*" refers in the expression "*b* as tonic"; and the presumable intent of the statement could then not be expressed. In short, the fact that in connection with wholes that are patterns or *Gestalts* of occurrences the word "sum" is either undefined, or defined in such a way that the whole is unequal to the sum of its parts, constitutes no inherently insuperable obstacle to analyzing such wholes into elements standing to each other in specified relations.

d. We must finally examine the use of "sum" in connection with wholes that are organized systems of dynamically interrelated parts. Let us assume as typical of such usage the statement "Although the mass of a body is equal to the sum of the masses of its spatial parts, a body also has properties that are not the sums of properties possessed by its parts." The comments that have just been made about "sum" in connection with patterns of occurrences such as melodies can be extended to the present context of usage of the word; and we shall not repeat them. In the present instance, however, an additional interpretation of "sum" can be suggested that may put into clearer light the content of such statements as the above.

When the behavior of a machine like a clock is sometimes said to be the sum of the behaviors of its spatial parts, what is the presumptive content of the assertion? It is reasonable to assume that the word "sum" does not here signifiy an unordered class of elements —for neither the clock nor its behavior is such a class. It is therefore plausible to construe the assertion as maintaining that from the theory of mechanics, coupled with suitable information about the actual arrangements of the parts of the machine, it is possible to deduce statements about the consequent properties and behaviors of the entire system. Accordingly, it seems also plausible to construe in a similar fashion statements such as that of J. S. Mill: "The different actions of a chemical compound will never be found to be the sums of actions of its separate parts."[5] More explicitly, this statement can be understood to assert that from some assumed theory concerning the constituents of chemical compounds, even when it is conjoined with appropriate data on the organization of these constituents within the compounds, it is not in fact possible to deduce statements about many of the properties of these compounds.

If we adopt this suggestion, we obtain an interpretation for "sum" that is particularly appropriate for the use of the word in contexts in which the wholes under discussion are organized systems of interdependent parts. Let T be a theory that is in general able to explain the occurrence and modes of interdependence of a set of properties P_1, P_2, . . . P_k. More specifically, suppose it is known that when one or more individuals belonging to a set K of individuals occur in an environment E_1 and stand to each other in some relation belonging to a class of relations R_1, the theory T can explain the behavior of such a system with respect to its manifesting some or all of the properties P. Now assume that some or all of the individuals belonging to K form a relational complex R_2 not belonging to R_1 in an environment E_2 which may be different from E_1, and that the system exhibits certain modes of behavior which are formulated in a set of laws L. Two cases may then be distinguished: from T, together with statements concerning the organization of the individuals in R_2, it is possible to deduce the laws L; or secondly, not all the laws L can be so deduced. In the first case, the behavior of the system R_2 may be said to be the "sum" of the behaviors of its component individuals; in the second case, the behavior of R_2 is *not* such a sum. It is evident that in a currently accepted sense of "reducible," the conditions for the reducibility of L to T are satisfied in the first case; in the second case, however, although one of these conditions may be satisfied, the other is not.

If this interpretation of "sum" is adopted for the indicated contexts of its usage, it follows that the distinction between wholes that are sums of their parts and those that are not is *relative to some assumed theory T* in terms of which the analysis of a system is undertaken. Thus, the kinetic theory of matter as developed during the nineteenth century was able to explain certain thermal properties of gases, including certain relations between the specific heats of gases. However, that theory was unable to account for these relations between specific heats when the state of aggregation of molecules is that of a solid rather than a gas. On the other hand, modern quantum theory is capable of explaining the facts concerning the specific heats of solids, and presumably also all other thermal properties of solids. Accordingly, although relative to classical kinetic theory the thermal properties of solids are not sums of the properties of their parts, relative to quantum theory those properties are such sums.

3. *Organic wholes.* We must now briefly consider what is the distinctive feature of those systems that are commonly said to be "organic unities" and that exhibit a mode of organization that is often claimed to be incapable of analysis in terms of an "additive

point of view." However, although living bodies are the most frequently cited examples of organic wholes, we shall not be now concerned specifically with such systems. For it is generally admitted that living bodies constitute only a special class of systems possessing a structure of internally related parts; and it will be an advantage to ignore for the present special issues connected with the analysis of vital phenomena.

Organic or "functional" wholes have been defined as systems "the behavior of which is not determined by that of their individual elements, but where the part-processes are themselves determined by the instrinsic nature of the whole."[6] What is distinctive of such systems, therefore, is that their parts do not act, and do not possess characteristics, *independently* of one another. On the contrary, their parts are supposed to be so related that any alteration in one of them causes a change in *all* of the other parts.[7] In consequence, functional wholes are also said to be systems which cannot be built up out of elements by combining these latter *seriatim* without producing changes in all those elements. Moreover, such wholes cannot have any part removed, without altering both that part and the remaining parts of the system.[8] Accordingly, it is often claimed that a functional whole cannot be properly analyzed from an "additive point of view"; that is, the characteristic modes of functioning of its constituents must be studied *in situ*, and the structure of activities of the whole cannot be inferred from properties displayed by its constituents in isolation from the whole.

A purely physical example of such functional wholes has been made familiar by Koehler. Consider a well-insulated electric conductor of arbitrary shape, for example one having the form of an ellipsoid; and assume that electric charges are brought to it successively. The charges will immediately distribute themselves over the surface of the conductor in such a way that the electric potential will be the same throughout the surface. However, the density of the charge (that is, the quantity of charge per unit surface) will not in general be uniform at all points of the surface. Thus, in the case of the ellipsoidal conductor, the density of the charge will be greatest at the points of greatest curvature and will be smallest at the points of least curvature.[9] In brief, the distribution of the charges will exhibit a characteristic pattern or organization—a pattern that depends on the shape of the conductor, but is independent of the special materials of its construction or of the total quantity of charge placed upon it.

But it is not possible to build up this pattern of distribution bit by bit, for example by bringing charges first to one part of the conductor and then to another so as to have the pattern emerge only after all the charges are placed on the conductor. For when a charge is placed on one portion of the surface, the charge will not remain there but will distribute itself in the manner indicated; and in consequence, the charge-density at one point is not independent of the densities at all other points. Similarly, it is not possible to remove some part of the charge from one portion of the surface without altering the charge-densities at all other points. Accordingly, although the total charge on a conductor is the sum of separable partial charges, the configuration of charge-densities cannot be regarded as composed out of independent parts. Koehler thus declares:

> The natural structure assumed by the total charge is not described if one says: at this point the charge-density is this much "and" at that point the density is that much, and so on; but one might attempt a description by saying: the density is so much at this point, so much at that point, all mutually interdependent, and such that the occurrence of a certain density at one point determines the densities at all other points.[10]

Many other examples—physical, chemical, biological, and psychological—could be cited that have the same intent as this one. There is therefore no doubt that there are many systems whose constituent parts and processes are "internally" related, in the sense that these constituents stand to each other in relations of mutual causal interdependence. Indeed, some writers have found it difficult to distinguish sharply between systems that are of this sort and systems that allegedly are not; and they have argued that all systems whatever ought to be characterized as whole that are "organic" or "functional" in some degree or other.[11] In point of fact, many who claim that there is a fundamental difference between functional and nonfunctional (or "summative") wholes tacitly admit that the distinction is based on *practical decisions* concerning what causal influences may be ignored for certain purposes. Thus, Koehler cites as an example of a "summative" whole a system of three stones, one each in Africa, Australia, and the United States. The system is held to be a summative grouping of its parts, because displacement of one stone has no effect on the others or on their mutual relations.[12] However, if current theories of physics are accepted, such a displacement is not without *some* effects on the other stones, even if the effects are so minute that they cannot be detected with present experimental techniques and can therefore be practically ignored.

Again, Koehler regards the total charge on a conductor as a summative whole of independent parts, though it is not at all evident that the electronic constituents of the charge undergo no alterations when parts of the latter are removed from it. Accordingly, although the occurrence of systems possessing distinctive structures of interdependent parts is undeniable, no general criterion has yet been proposed which makes it possible to identify in an absolute way systems which are "genuinely functional" as distinct from systems which are "merely summative."[13]

Moreover, it is essential to distinguish in this connection between the question whether a given system can be *overtly constructed* in a piecemeal fashion by a seriatim juxtaposition of parts, and the question whether the system can be *analyzed in terms of a theory* concerning its assumed constituents and their interrelations. There undoubtedly are wholes for which the answer to the first question is affirmative—for example, a clock, a salt crystal, or a molecule of water; and there are wholes for which the answer is negative—for example, the solar system, a carbon atom, or a living body. However, this difference between systems does not correspond to the intended distinction between functional and summative wholes, and our inability to construct effectively a system out of its parts, which in some cases may only be a consequence of temporary technological limitations, cannot be taken as evidence for deciding the second of the above two questions.

But let us turn to this second question, for it raises what appears to be the fundamental issue in the present context. That issue is whether the analysis of "organic unities" necessarily involves the adoption of irreducible laws for such systems, and whether their mode of organization precludes the possibility of analyzing them from the so-called additive point of view. The main difficulty in this connection is that of ascertaining in what way an "additive" analysis differs from one that is not. The contrast seems to hinge on the claim that the parts of a functional whole do not act independently of one another, so that any laws that may hold for such parts when they are not members of a functional whole cannot be assumed to hold for them when they actually are members. An "additive" analysis therefore appears to be one that accounts for the properties of a system in terms of assumptions about its constituents, where these assumptions are not formulated with specific reference to the characteristics of the constituents as elements in the system. And a "nonadditive" analysis seems to be one which formulates the characteristics of a system in terms of relations between certain of its parts as functioning elements in the system.

However, if this is indeed the distinction between these allegedly different modes of analysis, the difference is not one of fundamental principle. We have already noted that it does not seem possible to distinguish sharply between systems that are said to be "organic unities" and those that are not. Accordingly, since even the parts of summative wholes stand in relations of causal interdependence, an additive analysis of such wholes must include special assumptions about the actual organization of parts in those wholes when it attempts to apply some fundamental theory to them. There certainly are many physical systems, such as the solar system, a carbon atom, or a calcium fluoride crystal, that despite their complex form of organization lend themselves to an "additive" analysis; but it is equally certain that current explanations of such systems in terms of theories about their constituent parts cannot avoid supplementing these theories with statements about the special circumstances under which the constituents occur as elements in the systems. In any event, the mere fact that the parts of a system stand in relations of causal interdependence does not exclude the possibility of an additive analysis of the system.

The distinction between additive and nonadditive analysis is sometimes supported by the contrast commonly drawn between the particle physics of classical mechanics and the field approach of electrodynamics. It therefore will be instructive to dwell for a moment on this contrast. According to Newtonian mechanics, the acceleration induced in a particle by the action of other bodies is the vector-sum of the accelerations that would be produced by each of these bodies were they acting singly; and the assumption underlying this principle is that the force exerted by one such body is independent of the force exerted by any other. In consequence, a mechanical system such as the solar system can be analyzed additively. In order to account for the characteristic behavior of the solar system as a whole, we need to know only the force (as a function of the distance) that each body in the system exerts separately on the other bodies.

But in electrodynamics the situation is different. For the action of an electrically charged body on another depends not only on their distances, but also on their relative motions. Moreover, the effect of a change in motion is not propagated instantaneously, but with a finite velocity. Accordingly, the force on a charged body due to the presence of other such bodies is not determined by the positions and velocities of the latter, but by the conditions of the electromagnetic "field" in the vicinity of the former. In consequence, since such a field cannot be regarded as a "sum" of "partial" fields, each due to a distinct charged particle, an electromagnetic system is commonly said to be incapable of an additive analysis. "The field can be treated adequately only as a unit," so it is claimed, "not as the sum total of the contributions of individual point charges."[14]

Two brief comments must be made on this contrast. In the first place, the notion of "field" (as used in electromagnetic theory) undoubtedly represents a mathematical technique for analyzing phenomena that is different in many important respects from the mathematics employed in particle mechanics. The latter operates with discrete sets of state-variables, so that the state of a system is specified by a finite number of coordinates; the former requires that the values of each of its state-variables are specified for each point of a mathematically continuous space. And there are further corresponding differences in the kinds of differential equations, the variables that enter into them, and the limits between which mathematical integrations are performed.

But in the second place, though it is true that the electromagnetic field associated with a set of charged particles is not a "sum" of partial fields associated with each particle separately, it is also true that the field is uniquely determined (that is, the values of each state-variable for each point of space are unequivocally fixed) by the set of charges, their velocities, and the initial and boundary conditions under which they occur. Indeed, there is a technique employed within field theory, in the light of which the electromagnetic field is simply an intermediary device for formulating the effects of electrically charged particles upon other such particles.[15] Accordingly, though it may be convenient to treat an electromagnetic field as a "unit," this does not signify that the properties of the field cannot be analyzed in terms of assumptions concerning its constituents. And though the field may not be a "sum" of partial fields in any customary sense, an electromagnetic system is a "sum" in the special sense of the word proposed previously—namely, there is a theory about the constituents of these systems such that the relevant laws of the system can be deduced from the theory. In point of fact, if we take a final glance at the functional whole illustrated by the charges on the insulated conductor, the law which formulates the distribution of charge-densities can be deduced from assumptions concerning the behavior of charged particles.[16]

The upshot of this discussion of organic unities is that the question whether they can be analyzed from the additive point of view does not possess a general answer. Some functional wholes certainly can be analyzed in that manner, while in the case of others (for example, living organisms) no fully satisfactory analysis of that type has yet been achieved. Accordingly, the mere fact that a system is a structure of dynamically interrelated parts does not suffice, by itself, to prove that the laws of such a system cannot be reduced to some theory developed initially for certain assumed constituents of the system. This conclusion may be meager; but it does show that the issue under discussion cannot be settled, as so much of extant literature on it assumes, in a wholesale and a priori fashion.

NOTES

1. Bertrand Russell, *The Principles of Mathematics* (Cambridge: Cambridge University Press, 1903), p. 477.

2. An issue similar to the one raised by Russell has been raised in connection with the addition of velocities in relativity theory. Let A, B, C be three bodies, so that the velocity of A with respect to B is v_{AB}, that of B with respect to C is v_{BC} (where the direction of v_{BC} is parallel to the direction of v_{AB}), and of A with respect to C is v_{AC}. Then, according to classical mechanics, $v_{AC} = v_{AB} + v_{BC}$. But according to the special relativity theory,

$$v_{AC} = \frac{v_{AB} + v_{BC}}{1 + \frac{v_{AB} \cdot v_{BC}}{c^2}}$$

where *c* is the velocity of light. It has been argued that in the latter we are not "really adding" velocities. However, this objection can be disposed of in essentially the same manner as Russell's argument.

3. For an interesting sketch of a generalized formal analysis of Gestalts such as melodies, cf. Kurt Grelling and Paul Oppenheim, "Der Gestaltbegriff in Lichte der neuen Logik," *Erkenntnis*, 7:211–25 (1938).

4. Max Wertheimer, "Gestalt Theory," in Willis D. Ellis, *A Source Book of Gestalt Psychology* (New York: Harcourt, Brace, 1950), p. 5.

5. J. S. Mill, *A System of Logic* (London, 1879), Bk. III, Chap. VI, Sec. 2, Vol. I, p. 432.

6. Wertheimer, "Gestalt Theory," p. 2. Cf. also Koffka's statement: "Analysis if it wants to reveal the universe in its completeness has to stop at the wholes, whatever their size, which possess functional reality. . . . Instead of starting with the elements and deriving the properties of the wholes from them a reverse process is necessary, i.e. to try to understand the properties of parts from the properties of wholes. The chief content of Gestalt as a category is this view of the relation of parts and wholes involving the recognition of intrinsic real dynamic whole-properties." K. Koffka, "Gestalt," in *Encyclopedia of the Social Sciences* (New York, 1931), Vol. 6, p. 645.

7. Cf. Kurt Lewin, *Principles of Topological Psychology* (New York: McGraw-Hill, 1936), p. 218.

8. W. Koehler, *Die physischen Gestalten im Ruhe und im stationaeren Zustand* (Braunschweig, 1924), p. 42; also Ellis, *A Source Book of Gestalt Psychology*, p. 25.

9. More generally, the charge density on the ellipsoid is proportional to the fourth root of the curvature at a point.

10. W. Koehler, *Die physischen Gestalten*, p. 58, and cf. also p. 166. Many other physical examples of such "functional" wholes could be cited. The surfaces assumed by soap films provide an intuitively evident illustration. The gen-

eral principle underlying the analysis of such surfaces is that, subject to the boundary conditions imposed on the surface, its area is a minimum. Thus, neglecting gravity, a soap film bounded by a plane loop of wire will assume a plane surface; a soap bubble will assume the shape of a sphere, a figure which has the minimum surface for a given volume. Now consider a part of the surface of a soap bubble bounded by a circle. If this part were removable from the spherical surface, it would no longer retain its convex shape, but would become a plane. Thus, the shape assumed by a part of the film depends on the whole of which is a part. Cf. the account of soap film experiments in Richard Courant and Herbert Robbins, *What Is Mathematics?* (New York: Oxford, 1941), pp. 386ff.

11. This is the contention of A. N. Whitehead's philosophy of organism. Cf. his *Process and Reality* (New York: Humanities Press, 1929), especially Part II, Chaps. III and IV.

12. Koehler, *Die physischen Gestalten*, p. 47.

13. This suggestion that the distinction between functional and non-functional wholes is not a sharp one is borne out by an attempt to state more formally the character of an "organic" whole. Let S be some system and K a class of properties $P_1 \ldots P_n$ which S may exhibit. Assume, for the sake of simplicity of exposition, that these properties are measurable in some sense, so that specific forms of these properties can be associated with the values of numerical variables; and assume, also for the sake of simplicity, that statements about these properties have the form "At time *t* the property P_i of S has the value x" or more compactly, "$P_i(S,t) = x$." We now define a property in K, say P_1, to be "dependent" on the remaining properties in K when P_1 has the same value at different times if the remaining properties have equal values at those times—that is, when for every property P_i in K if $P_i(S,t_1) = P_i(S,t_2)$, then $P_1(S,t_1) = P_1(S,t_2)$. Moreover we shall say that the class K of properties is "interdependent" if *each* property in the class is dependent on the remaining properties in K—that is, when for every P_i and P_j in K, if $P_i(S,t_1) = P_i(S,t_2)$ then $P_j(S,t_1) = P_j(S,t_2)$.

On the other hand, we can define the class K to be an "independent" class if no property in K is dependent on the remaining properties of K. To fix our ideas, let S be a gas, V its volume, *p* its pressure, and T its absolute temperature. Then according to the Boyle-Charles law, V is dependent on *p* and T; and also this class of properties is an interdependent class of properties. Again, if S is an insulated conductor possessing a definite shape, R the curvature at any point, *s* the charge-density at any region, *p* the pressure at any region, then *p* is not dependent on R and *s*, and the set *p*,R and *s* do not form an interdependent class, though they do not form an independent class either. For this analysis, and further details involved in its elaboration, see the papers by Kurt Grelling, "A Logical Theory of Dependence," and by Kurt Grelling and Paul Oppenheim, "Logical Analysis of 'Gestalt' and 'Functional Whole,'" reprinted for members of the Fifth International Congress for the Unity of Science, held in Cambridge, Mass., in 1939, from the *Journal of Unified Science*, vol. 9. This volume of the *Journal* was a casualty of World War II and never appeared.

However, if now we define a system S to be a functional whole with respect to a class K of properties if K is an interdependent class, and also define S' to be a summative whole if K is an independent class, two points should be noted. In the first place, whether a property will be said to depend on certain others will depend in part on the degree of experimental precision with which values of the properties in question can be established. This is the point already made in the text. In the second place, though S may not be a functional whole in the sense defined, it need not therefore be a summative whole; for some properties in K may be dependent on the remaining ones, though not all are. Accordingly, there may be various "degrees" of interdependence of parts of a system.

14. Peter G. Bergmann, *Introduction to the Theory of Relativity* (New York: Prentice-Hall, 1942), p. 223. It would be pointless to ask in the present context whether any "physical reality" is to be assigned to electromagnetic fields or whether as some writers maintain the latter is only a "mathematical fiction." It is sufficient to note that whatever its "ultimate status," the field concept in physics represents a mode of analysis which can be distinguished from the particle approach.

15. The technique to which reference is made is the device of retarded potentials. Cf. the remarks in Max Mason and Warren Weaver, *The Electromagnetic Field* (Chicago: University of Chicago Press, 1929), Introduction.

16. Cf., for example, O. D. Kellogg, *Foundations of Potential Theory* (Berlin, 1929), Chap. VII.

Parts and Wholes in Language

Roman Jakobson

In the second part of Edmond Husserl's *Logische Untersuchungen* —still one of the most inspiring contributions to the phenomenology of language—two studies devoted to "Wholes and Parts" introduce the philosopher's meditations on "the Idea of Pure Grammar." In spite of the manifold aspects of interdependence between wholes and parts in language, linguists have been prone to disregard this mutual relationship.

Edward Sapir's *Totality*, the first and, unfortunately, almost the only completed installment of his projected general work on the *Foundations of Language* (1930), opens with a reference to the psychological factors which have hampered the analysis of whole-part relation: "(1) the feeling of rest or of inability to proceed after a count, formal or informal, has been made of a set or series or aggregation of objects; (2) the feeling of inability or unwillingness to break up an object into smaller objects."

The frequent inability of students in linguistics to go from a fractional totality to another totality that is higher or to another fraction that is lower has given rise to various isolationist trends in the science of language. For example, the outer, perceptible part of the sign, its *signans*, was examined deliberately without reference to the whole sign, which unites *signans* with *signatum*, that is, with the intelligible, translatable, semantic part of the total *signum*.

Another frequent limitation was to treat the *sentence* as the highest linguistic unit. Superior wholes, namely, *utterances*, which may embrace a higher integer of sentences, and the *discourse*, which normally is an exchange of utterances, remained outside the scope of linguistic analysis.

On the other hand, the sentence was often seen as the shortest actual verbal unit, while inferior entities such as the *word*, or at least its smallest meaningful constituent the *morpheme* (and, even more, its *phonemic* components), were considered mere scientific constructs imposed by scientists upon the verbal reality. The fact that all of these entities, from the *discourse* to its ultimate components (*distinctive features*), have quite different statuses in respect to the verbal code and present diverse degrees of relative dependence does not justify the attempts to exclude some of these units from the realistic and comprehensive portrayal of language as it actually is —a multistory hierarchy of wholes and parts. There is a certain reality, however, which corresponds to these restrictive scholarly attempts: what they mirror are the diverse types of grave language disturbances. These are pathological cases where speech is confined to one-sentence utterances or to the repetition of ready-made sentences, while the capacity to combine words into new sentences is entirely lost; or this ability may be preserved, but the derivational and inflectional operations are suppressed, because the patient is no longer able to manipulate the morphological constituents of the word. Finally, a stock of words may be retained, but recognition and reproduction of new words is impeded, because for the patient phonemic components cease to be an autonomous differential tool, whereby normal listeners and speakers can discern words never used and never heard before.

In his stimulating essay of this volume, Ernest Nagel endeavors to distinguish and delimit several types of the whole-part relation. It is noteworthy that each of these types plays a substantial role in the structure of language, and that a disregard for them threatens to distort and curtail the system.

As Nagel (1-f)* points out, "the word 'whole' may refer to a process, one of its parts being another process." The latest stage of speech analysis convincingly shows the importance of studying and correlating the different phases of the whole speech event, from source to destination: intention, innervation, gradual production, transmission, audition, perception, comprehension. Numerous examples of isolationist restriction of the study to a single phase of the process without reference to the subsequent phase, or cases of confusion and blendings between successive phases, have impeded analysis and deprived it of productive classificational criteria. The

* Letters at quotations from Nagel are those used in his chapter.

relative place of each phase within the whole process of speech requires adequate elucidation.

In another type of whole-part relation, the word whole "refers to some temporal period, whose parts are temporal intervals in it," and, as Nagel (1-b) stresses, neither wholes nor parts need be temporally continuous. The verbal message, for example, a sentence, is a temporal period, and its parts are temporal intervals within this whole. The parsing of a sentence, like linguistic analysis in general, must necessarily follow the principle of "immediate constituents," defined by Husserl and exhaustively elaborated in American linguistics.

These constituents are a clear example of virtually discontinuous parts, such as, for instance, the subject at the beginning and the verbal predicate at the end of the Mongolian sentence. On the other hand, every message may be and must be dealt with as a temporal interval within a verbalized or nonverbalized, continuous or discontinuous temporal context; and we stand before a nearly unexplored question of interrelation between message and context. In particular, the structural laws of ellipsis have not yet been subjected to a thorough analysis.

The comparison of incomplete and explicit messages, the fascinating problem of fragmentary propositions, challengingly outlined in Charles Peirce's perusal of "blanks" and in the semiotic studies of Frege and Husserl, strange as it may seem, have found no response among linguists. The artificial treatment of messages without reference to the superposed context once more exemplifies the illicit conversion of a mere part into a seemingly self-sufficient whole.

A contiguous question is the dependence of the message on the simultaneous environmental situation. Here the speech event is "spatially included" in a whole "with a spatial extension" (Nagel, 1-a). The spatio-temporal framework of the message becomes one of the crucial problems for any objective approach to language. From a realistic standpoint, language cannot be interpreted as a whole, isolated and hermetically sealed, but it must be simultaneously viewed both as a whole and as a part.

When Nagel (1-d) reminds us that the word "whole" may refer

"to a property of an object or process, and 'part' to some analogous property which stands to the first in certain specified relations," we can cite our previous example of the *signum* as the whole and the *signans* and *signatum* as its indispensably conjugated parts. Notwithstanding the experimental interest of their artificial separation in certain phases of linguistic scrutiny, the final aim of this analysis is the study of the two parts in relation to the whole of the sign.

If by "whole" we understand "any class, set, or aggregate of elements," then "part" may designate "either any proper subclass of the initial set or any element in the set" (Nagel, 1-c). The structure of the verbal code is perhaps the most striking and intricate example of whole-part relations that are built hierarchically. From the sentence model as a whole we go over to various syntactic patterns of sentences, on the one hand, and to the grammatical constituents of the sentence on the other. When we reach the level of the word, then either word classes or, again the morphological constituents of the word serve as parts. Gradually we arrive at the ultimate stage —the analysis of the smallest meaningful units into distinctive features. An important structural particularity of language is that at no stage of resolving higher units into their component parts does one encounter informationally pointless fragments.

The relation between a concrete object as whole and its properties as parts (Nagel, 1-g) is particularly typical of language, for not only is every classification of morphemes or complex grammatical units based on their abstract, semantic properties, but also each ultimate phonemic constituent, the distinctive feature, presents an abstract, relational, oppositive property.

Nagel's statement (1-e)—that "the word 'whole' may refer to a pattern of relations between certain specified kinds of objects or events, the pattern being capable of embodiment on various occasions and with various modifications"—finds a wide application in language with its relational invariants and manifold contextual and stylistic variations. This kind of whole-part relation, which was for a long time underrated by linguists, has finally attracted their attention, especially in regard to the contextual variants in phonemics and grammar. In the lexical field, which so far remains the underdeveloped province of linguistics, the study of invariance and of variables is still inferior to the medieval doctrine of the *modi significandi.*

Stylistic variations, particularly in phonology, gradually have begun to disturb students of language who had been until recently possessed by the isolationist idea of a monolithic verbal code. The variety of functional, mutually convertible subcodes requires a careful and consistent structural analysis. Such an analysis makes possible a synchronic study of the phonemic and grammatical changes in progress, which initially present a necessary coexistence of the older and newer form in two related subcodes, and thus there emerges a bridge between descriptive and historical linguistics. On the other hand, the inquiry into the system of subcodes encompasses the various forms of interdialectal and even interlingual code-switching and thus establishes an intimate bond between the description of an individual or local dialect and the vast horizons of linguistic geography.

If the whole is "a pattern of relations," then the part, as Nagel notices, may also refer to "any one of the elements which are related in that pattern on some occasion of its embodiment." Thus he touches upon the fundamental difference between design and token, a whole-part relation which linguists have recognized, but without drawing all the obvious and far-reaching inferences.

Finally, with the progress of typological studies, the science of language will be able to answer Nagel's question about systems "whose parts stand to each other in various relations of dynamical dependence" (1-h). The universal and near-universal laws of implication which underlie this taxonomy reveal a rigorous phonemic and grammatical stratification, which likewise determines the gradual acquisition of language by children and its decay in aphasia.

A systematic consideration of multiform whole-part relations broadly extends the scope of our science; it allows a systematic analysis of verbal messages in respect both to the code and to the context; it uncovers the complex interaction of the various levels of language, from the largest to the smallest units, and the constant interplay of diverse verbal functions. It introduces time and space factors into descriptive linguistics and, in searching for general, universal laws, is near to proving the scientific verity of Henri Delacroix's keen anticipation: "Une langue est une variation historique sur le grand thème humain du langage."

Indeed a rich scale of tensions between wholes and parts is involved in the constitution of language, where *pars pro toto* and, on the other hand, *totum pro parte, genus pro specie,* and *species pro individuo* are the fundamental devices.

"How Does a Poem Know When It Is Finished?"

I. A. Richards

I can set out from Edgar Allan Poe: "I have often thought how interesting a magazine paper might be written by an author who would—that is to say who could—detail, step by step, the processes by which one of his compositions attained its ultimate point of completion" (*The Philosophy of Composition*). "Who would—that is to say who could?" How are we to read that? Should it suggest that anyone able to give such an account would be only too happy to oblige? Or, on the contrary, that few could bear to make such an exhibition of themselves? The continuation of the passage rather leans toward the latter.

However that may be, is not perhaps a change of attitude here due? The brands of psychology that have been most widely distributed of late have been somewhat discouraging to our taste for privacy. The general notion that not even our own minds are our own—together with the view that there aren't any minds at all anyhow—would rather invite us to indulge in whatever exposures may, if so, prove possible. Accordingly, toward the end of this paper, you will find some sort of account of how one of my own poems attained—I won't say "its ultimate point of completion" but only the point at which it committed itself to burial in the page—hoping, of course, for innumerable lives thereafter, countless resurrections in its readers' minds.

My guide in much that I will be saying and assuming is Coleridge's remark, in Chapter XIV of *Biographia Literaria:* "Nothing can permanently please, which does not contain in itself the reason why it is so, and not otherwise." Or, as Shelley rephrased it in the opening sentence of *The Defense of Poetry:* "each containing within itself the principle of its own integrity."

It may be useful to consider, to begin with, that many poems (maybe all, but with the word "all" we are in danger of giving up observation in favor of definition, so I will say only "many") set themselves initially a problem, the solving, or dismission, or dispersal of which would be—in happy instances is—the completion: the attainment of the wholeness we are concerned with. Relative to that end (as terminus and as purposive goal) prior phrases—temporally or logically or psychologically or purposively prior in different instances—are parts.

Let us not try to be too specific, as yet, about these problems that poems set themselves. We may expect them to be illimitably various in innumerable respects, in character, in scope, in importance and in definiteness. Some of these problems are relatively simple; some relatively complex.

The type specimen of a simple and definite problem is, I take it, the drawing of a circle, which, as an exemplar of unity, must, I imagine, have been much used in this series of studies. The enterprise of drawing a freehand circle defines itself to itself very early—within the first millimeter of circumference drawn—and, with that, the conduct of all the rest of it and the criteria of success are uniquely prescribed and so is the exact point of completion.

Perhaps the minimal problem a poem can set itself is the mere finding or creation (discovery or invention) of a situation which will permit its growth. I have mentioned the word "growth" so early because I find myself deeply persuaded that the analogies that help most here are biological, organic, more specifically, embryological.

The over-all problem of any embryo was long ago described by the Psalmist—in the course of giving his own answer:

> Thine eyes did see my substance yet being unperfect;
> And in thy book were all my members written;
> Which day by day were fashioned:
> When as yet there was none of them.
>
> CXXXIX, 15–16

"When as yet there was none of them," how do they know what to become next in the course of becoming what in the end they have to be? That is the problem of the embryo. The answer offered is an analogy with a formula, an inventory, a sequence of directions, directives, in a book. It isn't really a good answer, is it? For one reason, because the very same problem appears if we ask: How does a set of directions, directives, in a book (how does a poem, for example) know what *it* must become next in the course of becoming what in the end it has to be?

We are beginning, I am told, to know enough about the chromosome dance to have some promise of knowing more or less how it works. We may expect that we will know all we need to know about that long, long before we will know nearly enough about the dance of words—and the dances behind their dancing—to get any adequate answer to our questions: "How does a poem grow? How does it learn how to become itself? How does it know when it is finished?"

Incidentally, this way of formulating the question is not, I think, an instance of the Pathetic Fallacy. As soon as the notice of this Colloquium went up, a friend greeted me with the remark: "You are a bold man to commit the Pathetic Fallacy in the title of a discussion!" But my title doesn't attribute anything to poems that they do not fully have. They are living, feeling, knowing *beings* in their own right; the so-called metaphor that treats a poem as organic is not a metaphor, but a literal description. A poem is an activity, seeking to become itself. All behavior (or activity, as I prefer to say: See *Speculative Instruments,* pp. 118–122) of organisms is organic. But of course, it must be *activity*. When we fall downstairs that is not activity; going up them is.

This view that poems, books, views, and so on, have some degree of self-responsibility—write their own tickets and pay for their own mistakes, and so on, can go too far. I remember Wittgenstein, soon after *Tractatus Logico-Philosophicus* was published, telling me there were two or three bad mistakes in it (not in the translation, he didn't complain of that, but in the thought). I innocently said: "Well, you can put in an errata slip and correct them in the second edition"—and found him staring at me as a Pillar of Society stares at a newly unmasked traitor: "How could I! It is my child! I could not murder it!" and so on.

Now to come a bit nearer to our specific question. Consider the word "father." How does it work? By a system of oppositions and collaborations with two other words: "mother" and "child."

I have chosen as evident an example as I can think of to illustrate mutual dependence of words on words. ("Center," "circumference," "circle" would be another example.) If I now add "husband," "wife," "family," we see, of course, that the mutual dependencies of words on words brought in by this change have now been immensely extended. We have jumped up from physiology to sociology, of course.

I have just used the words "of course." We all know, of course, that "of course" can be:

(1) a little gesture of modesty, a recognition of the audience's claim to intelligence
(2) an aggressive warning: "Differ from me if you dare!" *or*
(3) a self-comforting precaution against panic, or lots of other things besides, depending on the other words active (in the setting, in the then play of oppositions and collaborations) with "of course."

We could any of us go on indefinitely illustrating these oppositions and collaborations among words. All discourse illustrates them endlessly and inevitably. I would remind you here of two things:

(1) These collaborations and oppositions have to do not only with:

(T) What is Talked of.
(S) What is Said about it.
(D) How Distant we are to T and S.
(V) How we Value (+ or —) $\frac{T,S}{D}$ (thus Distanced)
(A) The *so what?* How we would Adjust something to us, and/or Adjust ourselves to it as result of
(O) How we would Organize all this in the interest of

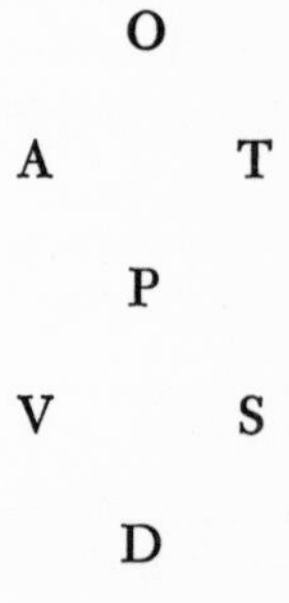

O
A T
P
V S
D

(P) The Purposive activity that is endeavoring to further itself in the poem. The collaborations and oppositions by which any utterance becomes whatever it is, and does whatever it does, are among all these.[1]

T, S
—
D
—
V (thus Valued)

(2) The other thing I would remind you of is this: language works not only by and through the words used but through words not used. Indignant Ruskin observed on one occasion, "I will not use the expressions which occur to me." Poems in various ways are always doing that. In poetry the rhyme-set, the alternates not adopted, the "root-forming morphemes" (*Interpretation in Teaching*, pp. 241–245) and so on through countless varieties of possible interaction, allowed or precluded. There is endless opposition and collaboration among words that do not appear at all: shaping, modifying, directing the activity of the growing poem at all points, guiding it and helping it to find out what has to be, and warning it when, if ever, it has become itself.

May I now be a little summary and dogmatic for a moment? A vast, recent aberration of concern with poets as subjects for biography has led too many to think that poems just express items, incidents, occurrences, crises, and so on, in a poet's experience. And here "experience" will mean *not* the imaginative, esemplastic activity of the growth of the poem, but some excerpt from a poet's everyday living: what he saw, felt or lived; what he did or what happened. I will not say it is never so (or we would again be, probably, just definition mongering) I will only say that we very rarely can have the sort of evidence that would be needed if we were really inquiring into this sort of question.

1. *See Speculative Instruments,* Chapter II "Towards a Theory of Comprehending" for a fuller account of these functions, or jobs, of language: the *respects* or *dimensions* or *factors* in which utterances may differ from one another. It will be clear that this analysis is supplementary to and not in conflict with such discussions as are offered in *Practical Criticism* in terms of Sense, Feeling, Tone, and Intention (pp. 180–188; 353–357).

The more usual thing—so far as available evidence goes—is for a poem, as I began by saying, to form at its inception a problem. The minimum problem I said was the finding, or creation, of a situation—a confluence of imaginative possibilities—able to support its growth. The situation, that confluence of possibilities, is a system of oppositions and collaborations among words. In brief, a poem begins by creating a linguistic problem whose solution by language will be the attainment of its end.

To make the peculiarly *linguistic* character of this problem more distinct let me contrast it explicitly both with the biographical problems just mentioned and with the literary or historical problems of a poem's genre or of its relations to earlier poems. The contrasts hold, although, and however much, all possible problems may, in a given instance, be interconnected. The methods, the concepts required, the direction and focus of attention exacted, the standards acceptable differ as we pass from one of these fields of perception and/or conjecture to another. Biographic speculations as to whatever in a poet's life shaped whatever in a poem must—at present, and very likely, always—have unassignable probabilities. Even when the poem *uses* verbal material, which is reported as having occurred in some biographically important incident, we would be rash to assume too confidently that the incident in any deep way determined the poem. Any sophisticated reader of good quality detective fiction would smile at such naive thinking in a Lestrade. The poem may just be using for its own purposes something that, in life, belonged in a different web. Yet biographic critics rarely show any such caution. The toils of their pursuit no doubt predispose them to overestimate their finds.

Comparative and historical studies, on the other hand, seem somewhat haunted by memories of burnt fingers. Early adventures in etymology, in folklore universalisms, in diffusionisms; examples from Frazer round to Freud seem to have had effect; humble pie has been widely served. The very elasticity of a genre has helped perhaps to discourage assertiveness. In brief, much scholarly reserve and mutual suspicion are to be observed.

Linguistic analysis, in contrast with both, mingles splash-happy recklessness with a methodological anxiety. Its dealings with archetypes, for example, range from one extreme to another. Bearing my title in mind, however, let me now look rather closely at a poem in which the mutual relevance of its parts—their oppositions and collaborations—seems rather more observable and describable than is usual. I hope thereby to bring out what one sort of linguistic account of the being of a poem may be like—not denying that there well may be other types of linguistic accounts and, still less, that biographic and literary-historical accounts may also be offered. Maybe the poet's correspondence, or notes preserved of his table talk, will enable some future biographer to write a very plausible short story about a possible process of composition for this poem. My point here is merely that, if so, it will be a short story to be placed properly in the genre, detective fiction.

As a springboard in this, let me use another sentence by Northrop Frye—from his address *Humanities in a New World* (Toronto, November 22, 1958). "The great writer seldom regards himself as a personality with something to say: his mind to him is simply a place where something happens to words." This, as it stands, looks like a generalization from biographies; but that, I think, is largely a *façon de parler*. Language invites us continually to talk about poets under conditions which only entitle us to talk about poems. The substance of this sentence, for me, is that well-organized poems can be studied as places where transactions between words take place. Let us then consider how "something happens to words," without further regard for the poet, in the instance of William Empson's

LEGAL FICTION*

Law makes long spokes of the short stakes of men.
Your well fenced out real estate of mind
No high flat of the nomad citizen
Looks over, or train leaves behind.

* From *Collected Poems*, copyright, 1935, 1940, 1949, by William Empson. Reprinted by permission of Harcourt, Brace & World, Inc. Also by permission of Chatto & Windus Ltd.

5 Your rights extend under and above your claim
Without bound; you own land in Heaven and Hell;
Your part of earth's surface and mass the same,
Of all cosmos' volume, and all stars as well.

Your rights reach down where all owners meet, in Hell's
10 Pointed exclusive conclave, at earth's centre
(Your spun farm's root still on that axis dwells);
And up, through galaxies, a growing sector.

You are nomad yet; the lighthouse beam you own
Flashes, like Lucifer, through the firmament.
15 Earth's axis varies; your dark central cone
Wavers a candle's shadow, at the end.

A topic sentence and then the rest of the poem an expansion, simultaneously literal and figurative. We need a diagram which we can easily draw for ourselves.

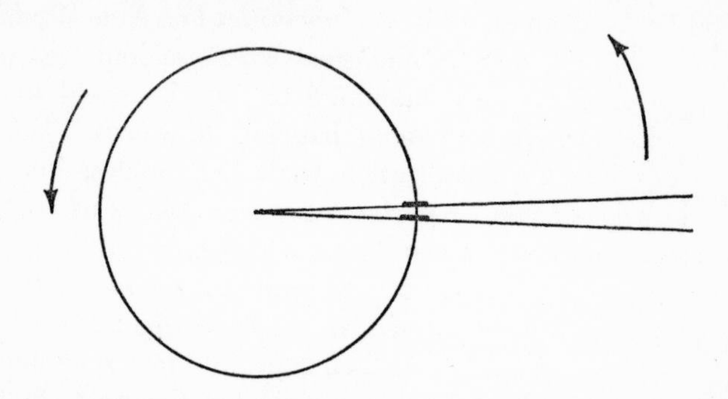

short stakes: Both the stakes the prospector drives in to mark the boundaries of his claim (1.5) and the posts of the fence that keeps cattle (say) in and trespassers out of the spun farm (1.11). Rights in this land include everything under and above 1.5)

They are *stakes,* too, in the sense in which a landowner is said to have a *stake* in the country. He has invested money, time and toil in his property; he has something *at stake.*

spokes: Because the earth rotates. (I am being thus explicit because in several classrooms I have met readers of high credentials who did not take this in.)

real estate of mind: The figurative meaning is being underlined: this is a state of mind and more, a set of mental acquisitions and developments, as much as it is a plot of earth. As such, its privacy is important.

No high flat: (however much of a skyscraper penthouse apartment it may be) can command this. Its heights and its depths are quite beyond any such survey. Though the poem itself may seem to be attempting something of the sort, the fourth verse reaffirms what this fourth line has asserted and adds indications as to why this is so, which are no small part of the completing movement.

nomad citizens: In contrast to the farmer (cultivating his garden). The fourth verse "comforts" this farmer, who may feel rather tied by his holding. He does a lot of travelling inevitably if his property is sweeping illimitably about in this fashion. It is a disturbing sort of comfort however: Lucifer is "fallen from heaven" (Isaiah, 14:12) and the self itself is shadowed by itself, hidden from whatever light it may produce.

you own land in Heaven and Hell: Both the conventional Heaven (and Dante's Inferno) *and* all that they betoken. Line 7 perhaps illustrates another sense of "unfinished" from that with which we are concerned: it seems to be in a rough, stop-gap, kind of state but line 9 picks up again with

where all owners meet, in Hell's/pointed exclusive conclave: A conclave is a locked-up place; specifically, the cardinals electing a pope. Behind the geometrical authority of the center (as determining the course of any circumference) there may be "the grand consult" of Milton's fallen Fiends as well as the uncomfortable communality of this joint possession—a high price, indeed a confiscatory price, to pay for being an owner.

What this sort of gloss should be attempting to bring out is the dependence of what any word or phrase can do in the poem upon what its other words and phrases can do there: the degree of their mutual enablement and mutual control. It is this—not any actions or agonies, any wishes or hopes or endeavors on the part of the poet or his readers—that settles what the poem may be and when and how (and whether) it is finished. The problem the poem invents (or discovers) is a linguistic problem in the sense that it is solved (and there are many sorts as well as modes of solution) through the collaborations of its constituent words. Any one reader, of course, is likely to enjoy, to participate in, but a portion of these. The same is true—as good poets have remarked—of the poet. It is arguable that in good poetry these collaborations among its words increase as the poem ages. The invention (or discovery) not only of the initial problem but of the derivative or resolving problems grows as, in imaginative study, what is happening in the poem relates itself to what has happened or could happen in other actual or possible poems. To compare poetry to a vastly simpler activity: a tennis player's game depends on other players.

The order of parts within a poem may change greatly during composition. Quite often, I believe, the first phrase to occur—the phrase to which the rest of the poem is a response—becomes, in the final version, the close. To illustrate the varying ways in which parts of a poem may league with one another, and invite different spatio-temporal arrangements to favor one set of alliances rather than another, here is a poem of my own in two arrangements: on the left a form in which it settled down enough to get on galley proofs; on the right a different sequence which a friend's arguments persuaded me to give it.

BY THE POOL*

In his meditation under the Bo tree, Gotama may have decided—in love and pity—to teach a doctrine which would do men good rather than another doctrine which few only could follow.

Not beneath the Bo tree
—Its long-tongued leaves
Poplar-like a-flutter—
This Buddha sits;
But by a limpid water
Welling by;

There search-winds of heaven
Twirl an imploring leaf,
Set the whole tree a-shiver
In glory, in grief:
Beneath, the All-giver
In pity willed
To bind up the Sheaf.

* From *The Screens and Other Poems*, © 1959, 1960, by I. A. Richards. Reprinted by permission of Harcourt, Brace & World, Inc. Also by permission of Routledge & Kegan Paul Ltd.

Which maybe more befits
Words none will utter
9 Whoever sigh.

10 There search-winds of heaven
Twirl an imploring leaf,
Set the whole tree a-shiver
In glory, in grief:
Beneath, the All-giver
In pity willed
To bind up the Sheaf.

Here by his River
That tumult's stilled.

Truly inaudible
20 —Yet to be heard
By the ear of the mind—
The penultimate word,
Ultimate quibble:

Not ours to bind,
That way the sword;
Who lay aside the cord
They alone find.

The still figure
Beyond the flow
Listens, listened
Aeons ago.
Ever a-flutter
Must all words be.

Here is an end.

Here by his River
That tumult's stilled.

Not ours to bind,
That way the sword;
Who lay aside the cord
They alone find.

Not beneath the Bo tree
—Its long-tongued leaves
Poplar-like a-flutter—
This Buddha sits;
But by a limpid water
Welling by;
Which maybe more befits
Words none will utter
Whoever sigh.

Truly inaudible
—Yet to be heard
By the ear of the mind—
The penultimate word,
Ultimate ripple.

The still figure
Beyond the flow
Listens, listened
Aeons ago.
Ever a-flutter
Must all words be.

Here is an end.

I presented the versions in parallel so to my audience in the Colloquium with some remarks suggesting that the right-hand column should be regarded as a final form replacing an imperfect first draft printed on the left. This mode of treating the poem naturally put it on its mettle and, accordingly on the following day, it asserted its independence anew and reconstituted itself—reverting to the left hand version with these exceptions: lines 24–27 moved up to precede line 19, and in line 23 *ripple* replaced *quibble.*

Two remarks in conclusion: (1) The completion of a poem may be no matter of addition or excision, or of change in phrasing—though the change of one word may induce very extensive changes in the oppositions and collaborations among the other words. The completion may depend upon questions of sequence among parts otherwise seemingly invariant. Similarly, heightened attention to one word may lead to great changes in the mutual enablements of other words. Meter and rhyme are, of course, a poem's chief controls whereby words can be accorded attention or protected from it: brought forward or distanced.

(2) Whatever the author may think himself entitled to do to a poem, the poem itself has the last word. It alone knows its duty. Authors, therefore, in their role as critics, will be wise to pay particular attention to the dangers of misreading their own lines. The poem in its "persuasive continuity"—to use a phrase from Northrop Frye—is one thing. As frozen for critical examination it is another. The examining eye—the descriptive instrument or screen by which it is held stable for observation and appraisal—can and frequently does deform it. The proper moral to draw might be: *Let us not lose the poem in our account of it.* This may free the poem from much interference; but does not deprive it of any help afforded by light reflected from even mistaken critical opinions.

NOTES ON CONTRIBUTORS

ROMAN JAKOBSON, born in Moscow in 1896, is Professor of Slavic Languages and Literatures at Harvard University and visiting Institute Professor at Massachusetts Institute of Technology. He received his A.B. from Lazarev Institute of Oriental Languages, his first degree diploma from Moscow University, and his Ph.D. from Prague University. He holds an honorary M.A. from Harvard University. A scholar of international reputation, his works in English include: *Russian Epic Studies* (with E. J. Simmons); *Preliminaries to Speech Analysis* (with G. Fant and M. Halle); and *Fundamentals of Language.*

CLYDE KLUCKHOHN, late Professor of Anthropology at Harvard University, was recognized as one of the great men in American science. He was the author of *Anthropology and the Classics; The Navaho; Children of the People* (with D. Leighton, M.D.); *Personality in Nature, Society and Culture* (with H. Murray, M.D.); *Mirror for Man; Navaho Means People* (with E. Z. Vogt and Leonard McCombe); and *How the Soviet System Works* (with R. Bauer and A. Inkeles). Some of his numerous journal essays are included in *Culture and Behavior,* published posthumously.

SIMON KUZNETS, born in Kharkov, Russia, in 1901, is Professor of Political Economy at the Johns Hopkins University. In addition to a B.S. from Columbia, M.A. and Ph.D. from Princeton, and D.Sc. from Harvard, he holds several honorary degrees: D.H.L. from Columbia, D.Sc. from Princeton, and D.Sc. in Economics from the University of Pennsylvania. He is the author of *Secular Movements in Production and Prices; National Income and Its Composition; Economic Change; Six Lectures on Economic Growth;* and many other works. He has served as a member of the staff of the National Bureau of Economic Research, and as Associate Director of the Bureau of Planning and Statistics of the W.P.B.

DANIEL LERNER, born in New York City in 1917, is Ford Professor of Sociology and International Communication at the Massachusetts Institute of Technology, and a Senior Research Associate of its Center for International Studies. During World War II he served as Chief Editor of the intelligence branch of the Psychological Warfare Division, SHAEF, and as Chief of Intelligence in the Information Control Division of the Office of Military Government, U.S.A. His books include *Sykewar; Propaganda in War and Crisis; The Nazi Elite; The Policy Sciences* (with H. D. Lasswell); *France Defeats EDC* (with Raymond Aron); and *The Passing of Traditional Society.*

Ernest Nagel, born in Novemesto, Czechoslovakia, in 1901, is Professor of Philosophy at Columbia University. He received his B.S. from the City College of New York, and his A.M. and Ph.D. from Columbia. His works include *On the Logic of Measurement; Sovereign Reason; Logic without Metaphysics;* and *Gödel's Proof* (with J. R. Newman). He has served as editor of the *Journal of Philosophy,* the *Philosophy of Science,* and the *Journal of Symbolic Logic,* and is a frequent contributor to these and other learned journals.

Edward Purcell, born in Taylorville, Illinois, in 1912, is Professor of Science at Harvard University. He received his B.S. from Purdue University and his A.M. and Ph.D. from Harvard. During World War II he served as the leader of the Fundamental Developments Group at Radiation Laboratory, Massachusetts Institute of Technology, and later was a member of the President's Scientific Advisory Committee. He was awarded the Nobel Prize in Physics for 1952.

Simon Ramo is executive vice president of Thompson Ramo Wooldridge, Inc. He received his B.S. from the University of Utah and his Ph.D. from the California Institute of Technology. Dr. Ramo attained prominence for his work in microwaves, electron optics, and traveling waves in electron streams and, later, in the development of fire control systems and missiles. He is the author of *Fields and Waves in Modern Radio* (with John R. Whinnery) and *Introduction to Microwaves,* and has edited and contributed to numerous publications. He has served as a consultant to committees assisting the United States Government, and is a member of the Scientific Advisory Board of the Air Force.

I. A. Richards was born in 1893 in Sandbach, Cheshire, England. He attended Clifton College and then Cambridge, where he read Moral Sciences and taught English Literature—publishing, among other books, *Principles of Literary Criticism* and *Practical Criticism.* He wrote no verse until his sixty-first year. He is at present a University Professor at Harvard. His recent publications include *A Leak in the Universe; Goodbye Earth and other Poems;* and *The Screens and Other Poems.*

Guide to Further Readings

IN ECONOMICS

IN THE LIGHT of Professor Kuznets' paper, it is especially instructive to reread Books I and II (chapter 1–7) of J. M. Keynes, *The General Theory of Employment, Interest and Money* (New York: Harcourt, Brace, 1935). In Book I Keynes restates the postulates and principles of classical economics as an operational set of analytic categories. In Book II he discusses "the choice of units" (though from another perspective than Kuznets), identifies "expectation" as a determinant context, and gives operational definition to his own use of the key terms income, saving, and investment.

Joseph Schumpeter presents a fascinating essay on the way new conceptions of "the whole" historically transformed economists' understanding of the "the parts" in *Economic Doctrine and Method* (London: Allen and Unwin, 1957). In Chapter 2, entitled "The Discovery of the Circular Flow of Economic Life," he argues that this discovery of "the whole" economic process was "the great breach through which lay all further progress in the field of analysis."

Readers interested in economic part-whole relations over a time dimension will do well to read the title essay in Jacob Viner, *The Long View and the Short* (New York: The Free Press of Glencoe, 1958). This is followed by "The Role of Costs in a System of Economic Liberalism"—a nice illustration of the variations discernible in a "part" (i.e., costs) when the contextual "whole" is shifted (i.e., a different system is postulated).

IN ANTHROPOLOGY

The reader who wishes to test this model against full substantive materials is advised to begin with the following sources:

ALBERT, ETHEL. "The Classification of Values," *American Anthropologist,* 58 (1956), 221–248.

KLUCKHOHN, C., and WYMAN, L. C. *An Introduction to Navaho Chant Practice* (Memoir 53), American Anthropological Association, 1940.

KLUCKHOHN, C. "Navaho Categories," in Diamond, David (Ed.), *Culture in History,* New York: Columbia University Press, 1960.

LADD, J. *The Structure of a Moral Code,* Cambridge, Mass.: Harvard University Press, 1956.

REICHARD, G. A. *Navaho Religion* (2 vols.), New York: Pantheon Books, Inc., 1950.

SPENCER, KATHERINE. *Mythology and Values, Memoirs of the American Folklore Society,* Vol. 48, 1957.

IN SYSTEMS ENGINEERING

ASHBY, W. R. *Design for a Brain,* New York: John Wiley & Sons, Inc., 1954.

BENDAT, J. S. *Principles and Applications of Random Noise Theory,* New York: John Wiley & Sons, Inc., 1958.

CHERRY, C. *On Human Communication,* New York: John Wiley & Sons, Inc., 1957.

CHURCHMAN, C. W., ACKOFF, R. L., and ARNOFF, E. L. *Introduction to Operations Research,* New York: John Wiley & Sons, Inc., 1958.

FELLER, W. *Probability Theory and Its Applications,* New York: John Wiley & Sons, Inc., 1950.

FRY, T. C. *Probability and Its Engineering Uses,* Princeton, N.J.: D. Van Nostrand Co., Inc., 1928.

GOLDMAN, S. *Information Theory,* Englewood Cliffs, N.J.: Prentice-Hall, Inc., 1954.

GOODE, H. H., and MACHOL, R. E. *Systems Engineering,* New York: McGraw-Hill Book Co., Inc., 1957.

GRABBE, E. M., RAMO, S., and WOOLDRIDGE, D. E. *Handbook of Automation, Computation, and Control:* Vol. I, *Control Fundamentals* (1958); Vol. II, *Computers and Data Processing* (1959); Vol. III, *Systems and Components* (1960), New York: John Wiley & Sons, Inc.

JERGER, J. J. *Systems Preliminary Design,* Princeton, N.J.: D. Van Nostrand Co., Inc., 1960.

MORSE, P. M., and KIMBALL, G. E. *Methods of Operations Research,* New York: John Wiley & Sons, Inc., 1956.

PIERCE, J. R. "Communication Theory," *Physics Today,* 4 (1951), 5.

SHANNON, C. E., and MCCARTHY, J. (Eds.). *Automata Studies* (Annals of Mathematical Studies, No. 34), Princeton, N.J.: Princeton University Press, 1956.

SHANNON, C. E., and WEAVER, W. *The Mathematical Theory of Communication,* Urbana, Ill.: University of Illinois Press, 1949.

TRUXAL, J. G. *Automatic Feedback Control System Synthesis,* New York: McGraw-Hill Book Co., Inc., 1955.

TSIEN, H. *Engineering Cybernetics,* New York: McGraw-Hill Book Co., Inc., 1954.

Von Neumann, J. "The General and Logical Theory of Automata," Jeffress, L. A. (Ed.), *Cerebral Mechanisms in Behavior,* New York: John Wiley & Sons, Inc., 1951.

IN PHILOSOPHY

Bertalanffy, L. von. *Modern Theories of Development,* New York: Oxford University Press, 1933. Chapter 6.
Campbell, N. R. *Measurement and Calculation,* New York: Longmans, Green & Co., Inc., 1928.
Johnson, W. E. *Logic,* New York: Cambridge University Press, 1922. Part II, Chapter 7.
Mill, J. S. *A System of Logic,* Book III, Chapter 6.
Petermann, B. *The Gestalt Theory,* Book II, Part I, London: Routledge, 1932. Chapter 1.
Russell, B. *The Principles of Mathematics,* Cambridge: Cambridge University Press, 1903, p. 477.
Torgerson, W. S. *Theory and Methods of Scaling,* New York: John Wiley & Sons, Inc., 1958.
Woodger, J. H. *Biological Principles,* London: Routledge, 1929. Chapter 6.

IN LANGUAGE

Delacroix, H. *Le language et la pensée,* Paris, 1924.
Frege, G. *Philosophical Writings,* Oxford, 1952.
Husserl, E. *Logische Untersuchungen,* II, Halle, 1902.
Peirce, C. S. *The Simplest Mathematics, Collected Papers of Charles Sanders Peirce,* IV, Cambridge, Mass.: Harvard University Press, 1933.
Sapir, E. *Totality, Language Monographs,* No. 6. Linguistic Society of America, 1930.
Whorf, B. L. *Language, Thought and Reality: Selected Writings,* Carroll, J. B. (Ed.), New York: John Wiley & Sons, Inc., 1956.

IN POETRY

Brower, R. A. (Ed.), *On Translation* (contributions by R. Jakobson and Hollander), Cambridge, Mass.: Harvard University Press, 1959.
Empson, W. *Structure of the Complex Word,* London: Chatto and Windus Ltd.
Jakobson, R., and Halle, M. *Fundamentals of Language,* Mouton, the Hague; New York: Humanities Press.

LEWIS, C. S. *Studies in Words,* New York: Cambridge University Press, 1960.

MACLEISH, A. *Poetry and Experience,* Boston: Houghton Mifflin Company, 1961.

RICHARDS, I. A. "The Future of Poetry," in *The Screens and Other Poems,* New York: Harcourt, Brace & World, Inc., 1960.

RICHARDS, I. A. *Speculative Instruments,* Chicago: University of Chicago Press, 1955.

SEBEOK, T. A. (Ed.), *Style in Language,* Cambridge, Mass.: Technology Press, Massachusetts Institute of Technology; New York: John Wiley & Sons, Inc., 1960.